DIY Solar Power

Written by
Micah Toll

Cover design and diagrams by Micah Toll.

Printed in the United States of America
Toll Publications, 2018
ISBN-13 978-0-9899067-1-5

To my wife Sapir, who humors me …

Table of Contents

Chapter 1: Introduction

Note: While it may be tempting to skip around this book from section to section, or jump directly to the chapter that most interests you, I highly recommend that you read this book in order, starting with Chapter 1. I will be teaching you a number of different concepts throughout this book. Each of the concepts build on each other and are critical to building a safe, practical and efficient solar powered setup. By skipping sections, you may miss out on important material covered earlier the book. It's just a suggestion, but I recommend that you take it!

The idea of capturing solar energy from the sun has always fascinated me. And if you're reading this book, then I imagine you share my deep interest in harnessing the power of the sun.

Solar energy feels to me like the closest thing we'll ever have to "free", abundant energy. The sun is a gigantic fusion reactor, creating energy by fusing hundreds of millions of hydrogen atoms into helium every second of every day. It never stops and it never sleeps. It just continues working tirelessly and waiting for us to take advantage of it.

The amount of energy from the sun landing on an area the size of a tennis court in just one hour is enough to power an average US home for three days. The energy is there and it's ripe for the taking. We just have to make use of it instead of letting it go to waste, baking the asphalt and dirt.

The good news is that it's actually quite easy. Humans have been harnessing the power of the sun in one way or another for thousands of years. Buddhist scripture from over 2,500 years ago describes the use of the sun to evaporate sea water in India to harvest sea salt. The ancient Greeks and Romans used mirrors to reflect light from the sun, concentrating its power to make fire and light torches. It is even claimed that the Greek scientist Archimedes used mirrors as a tool of war, concentrating the sun with enough strength to set fire to besieging Roman ships.

These are all impressive examples of human ingenuity used to capture the power of the sun. And one thing they all have in common is that they use no electricity! They are all completely passive solar projects, taking advantage simply of the heat provided by the sun. In this book we will of course be talking a lot about electricity generated by solar power and its uses, but I also want to point out and discuss the amazing potential of passive solar energy and how you can easily capture and use it for your own needs. We'll be covering both concepts in this book, solar electric power and passive solar, as they are both useful for different types of projects and circumstances.

Let's start with solar electric power, as that is the one most people think of when they discuss solar power.

Solar electricity

Electricity can be generated from the sun's rays in a few different ways. The most common method is to use photovoltaic cells. Photovoltaics, or PVs, are specialized semiconductors that convert photons, or high energy light particles that originate from the sun, into an electrical current. In this case, the current is known as Direct Current, or DC electricity, but we'll talk about that more in Chapters 2 and 3. For now, we'll just stick with the basics. When light hits a PV cell, it causes the PV cell to produce electricity that we can use to power our devices.

The first PV cells were developed in laboratories as early as the 1880's, though they were crude prototypes made from selenium and created very little electricity. Most scientists of the day considered them little more than a novelty. It wasn't until the 1950's that scientists at Bell Laboratories accidentally discovered a method to create a stronger and more robust photovoltaic cell when they began to experiment with silicon for transistors. The discovery of silicon PV cells jumpstarted research, and soon the US government came knocking, interested in the ability of PV cells to power satellites. With more money and demand, research intensified and scientists continued to improve the efficiency of PV cells over time by mixing in different chemicals with the silicon slices and chips.

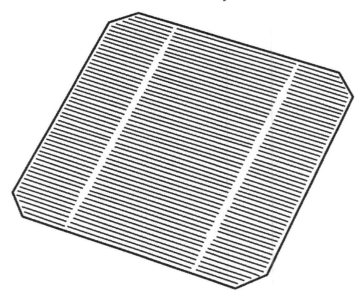

A single photovoltaic cell

The Oil Crisis of 1973 saw the price of oil skyrocket almost overnight, making what had previously been expensive solar panels suddenly much more attractive. Soon, these solar panels were being used for applications where it was too expensive or even impossible to run existing electrical wiring, such as remote areas, boats, and space exploration projects.

Increased production and supply of PV cells over the next few decades helped the price of solar panels drop quickly, from around $75/watt in the late 1970's to $7.50/watt by the late 1980's. However, the price stayed fairly steady throughout the 1990's and early 2000's until huge surpluses from China flooded the market, further driving down prices. As of 2018, it is possible to buy PV cells for around $0.50 per watt directly from China, though fully assembled panels usually cost closer to $1-$2/watt, depending on the size and quantity purchased. For relatively large 100 W panels, the price is usually approximately $1/watt when purchasing directly from China, with smaller panels costing somewhat more per watt.

As the price for solar panels has plummeted, their adoption has skyrocketed. More affordable PV cells have made it easier than ever to power devices using electricity generated directly from the sun. The beauty of electricity generated by PV cells is that it is no different than any other electricity. While there are some important electronics concepts that we'll discuss in Chapter 2, for the most part, all electricity is essentially the same and your cell phone or refrigerator doesn't care if the electricity was generated from burning coal or the burning sun, as long as the electricity has the correct voltage and current parameters (which again, we'll be talking about soon – let's not get ahead of ourselves!).

However, PV cells aren't the only way to generate electricity from the sun. They are a direct method to convert photons to electrical current, but there are other indirect methods to achieve the same goal. Another common method uses an array of many mirrors, each set to track the sun and reflect its light to a common point, usually elevated on a tower. The light is concentrated on a single point, often containing a tank of water. As the water boils and becomes superheated, it turns to steam that then flows through a turbine. The turbine spins, generating electricity, and the steam is condensed back into water to flow back into the tank to be reheated, continuing the cycle. This is similar to the way electricity is produced using coal or natural gas, which are burned to boil water and create steam. The only difference with our method is that instead of using fossil fuels to power a boiler, we're using the power of the sun instead. Why pay for fuel when the sun is free?!

Non-electrical solar energy (passive solar)

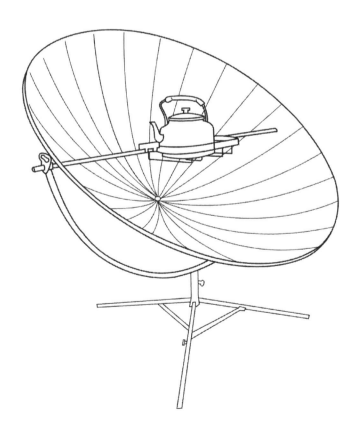

Parabolic dish solar cooker

The practice of using mirrors to reflect and concentrate the sun's energy isn't just applicable on large scale projects like massive heating towers. You can collect solar energy at home too, and without needing to generate any electricity! Many people all over the world use solar ovens to cook food. By using the same concept of redirecting and concentrating the sun's energy, people can boil water or heat food with the power of the sun instead of burning wood or charcoal. This also helps by reduce pollution from thousands of cooking fires, as well as decreasing deforestation in many sensitive areas of the world.

Solar cookers and ovens come in many different varieties. A common solar cooker setup uses a curved mirror that looks like a satellite dish. A pot is placed in the center and the entire apparatus is pointed at the sun. The sun's rays are reflected off of the interior of the dish and concentrated on the pot in the center, heating it to cook food or boil water.

Solar ovens are usually boxier, but have a wide top with reflective panels that collect sunlight and bounce it into the box. A glass top helps keep the heat in, creating a greenhouse effect. Reflective walls inside the box ensure that light reflects until it hits the food in the center of the box, cooking it similarly to a conventional oven.

Other uses of solar energy for heating include passive solar water heaters. Israel, a country with limited traditional energy resources but an abundance of sun, has one of the highest rates of solar powered water heaters in the world. After experiencing a significant nationwide energy shortage in the 1950's and 60's, many people turned to passive solar water heating to provide hot water for their homes. This worked so well that the Israeli government eventually passed a law making it mandatory to install passive solar water heaters on all residential buildings, a decision that has saved hundreds of millions of dollars ever since.

Thermosiphon passive solar water heater

Solar water heaters are simple devices that require no electricity at all, and can be used effectively in many parts of the world. Municipal water flows up to a tank on the roof of a home, where it then flows through a series of pipes, usually painted black, which are angled towards the sun. The intense heat of the sun quickly heats the water in the pipes, which becomes less dense as it gets hotter. The hot water then reaches the tops of the pipes and flows into the storage tank. When it's time for a shower, the hot water on the roof is supplied and the homeowner gets a nice, hot shower without the need for any electricity.

In colder environments, the storage tank might need to be located inside the home instead of on the roof, but the system still works nearly the same. The only difference is that a small electrical pump is needed to move the water around between the heating pipes and the storage tank. There are also some other variations on solar water heaters, and we'll discuss those in more detail in Chapter 11.

Another great use of passive solar is to heat the water in a pool or hot tub. This is even easier, as the water can directly flow through the heating pipes and back into the storage tank, which in this case is your pool or hot tub, on a continuous loop. The time spent in the heating pipe controls the temperature of the water. Many people build these types of solar water heaters completely by themselves using flexible black pipe or hose, coiled in dark box with a clear lid, and a small electrical pump. It's one of the easiest DIY passive solar projects you can make, and perhaps one of the most enjoyable too!

I hope this introduction has given you an overview of the power of harnessing energy from the sun, and the many different ways this is possible. Now that we understand where we are headed, we can take a deep dive into all of these topics and more in the coming chapters. We'll start with solar electricity generation, but first we'll need to learn the basics of electricity. Join me in Chapter 2, where I break these concepts down simply and easily to help you quickly grasp the important concepts relevant to all electrical circuits!

Chapter 2: The basics of electricity

The most common use of solar energy is capturing it and converting it to electricity. But before we can do that, we need to understand how this electricity works. Don't worry though, the concepts are actually quite simple and you don't need to be an electrical engineer to understand them. Let's go through them together now.

First of all, we'll define electricity. All you need to know is that electricity is just a type of energy that consists of a flow of electrons, which are little charged particles. The important point to take away from this definition is that electricity is a flow of charge. Electricity *flows*.

There are two common analogies that are often used for describing how electricity works: the water model and the car model. Let's look at both, and you can choose to use whichever one works better for you.

In the water model, think about a hose or pipe that contains flowing water. That water is your electricity. If you'd like, you can think about each drop of water as an electron, which is just a bit of charge. But you don't have to get too specific. We've got a hose with flowing water, and this is our electrical hose. The hose is basically a wire and the water is basically the electricity.

In the car model, think about a road or a highway with cars traveling along it. The road is like a wire and the cars are the electricity flowing along through it. In this case, each car could be an electron. The road is full of cars and they are all driving down the road together. This highway represents our flow of electricity - an electrical highway, if you will.

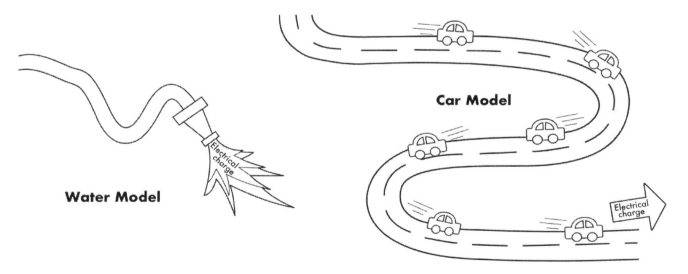

I'm partial to the water model myself, but as we go through each electrical concept below, feel free to use whichever model makes more sense to you.

The two most important parameters related to electricity are voltage and current. We'll start with voltage.

Voltage

Voltage is a measure of electrical force, measured in the units of volts. In the water model, voltage is like the water pressure in the hose. Low voltage means that there is very little force in the flow of electrons in the electricity. That's just like low water pressure in a hose, where water slowly dribbles out of the end of the hose due to the low pressure. But what if you open up the valve on your hose and increase the water pressure? That would be like high voltage, where now there's a lot of electrical force (or a lot of water pressure in our analogy) in the flow of the electricity. Or if you prefer the car model, high voltage is like cars driving really fast down the highway, and low voltage is like a road full of old grannies driving really slowly.

Higher voltage has higher electrical force. This means that the electrons in the flow really want to, well… *flow*. This also makes higher voltage more dangerous. Think about a simple battery, like a AA battery for a flashlight or TV remote control. Standard alkaline AA batteries are 1.5 V, or one and a half volts. If you've ever played around with one, then you might have tried connecting the two ends with a wire and seen a little spark. That little spark is quite small though and often hard to see. This is because the voltage is low, at just 1.5 V. The low voltage means low electrical force, or a weak flow of electricity. So you might get a little spark, which is the sudden flow of electrons, but it's not very impressive.

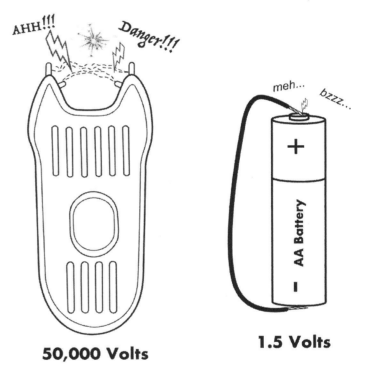

50,000 Volts

1.5 Volts

Where have you seen bigger sparks before? Think about a taser, which is a weapon that can create an impressive (and scary) arc of electricity sparking between two electrodes. Most tasers use tens of thousands of volts. A 50,000 V taser makes a much bigger spark than a 1.5 V battery, because the higher voltage means there is a lot more electrical force, creating a much bigger spark (or much greater flow of electricity through the air).

You can also feel differences in voltage. If you've ever touched two wires from a 1.5 V battery such as a AA battery to your tongue, you'll feel a slight sensation, and maybe even get a slight copper taste on your tongue. That's the flow of electricity across your tongue. Ever try licking a 9 V battery? I don't recommend it, but it's a quick way to determine if a 9 V battery is dead or still has some juice left. However, you'll get a much stronger sensation from a 9 V battery than you did from that 1.5 V battery, since there is six times the electrical force in that 9 V battery, meaning six times the flow of electricity is passing through your tongue. Yikes!

Note: You should never lick any batteries, but if you do, you should <u>definitely</u> never lick batteries higher than 9 V. There's a reason that tasers are considered weapons - they're dangerous and painful.

Ok, so I think you understand how voltage works. It's electrical force, or the force of the flow of electricity. It's the water pressure in the hose, or the speed of the cars on the highway. And now I've beaten that horse dead, right? Good, now let's look at current.

Current

Current is the *rate* of flow of electricity. To put it another way, current is the amount of charge passing through any point along the flow. Current is measured in amperes, which we usually just call amps for short.

To better understand what current is, let's go back to our models, starting with the water model. Imagine two hoses: a small diameter garden hose and a big fat fire hose. We could use both to fill a swimming pool, but the fire hose is going to fill the pool much faster than the garden hose, right? That's because the water in the fire hose has a higher rate of flow than the water in the garden hose. If you hooked up a flowmeter to the two hoses, you might find that the garden hose has a flow of flow rate of 100 liters per minute, while the fire hose has a flow rate of 500 liters per minute. In our analogy, since the flow rate is effectively our current, the garden hose is like electricity flowing with lower current, or amps, while the fire hose is like electricity flowing with higher current, or amps.

If you want to use the car analogy, imagine a four lane interstate highway versus a single lane country road. The wide interstate has more lanes and will let more cars through at once compared to the single lane road, even if the cars are traveling at the same speed on both roads. So the interstate would be high current, while the single lane highway would be lower current.

Both of these analogies aren't 100% exact, as electricity is a bit more complicated than water flowing or cars driving, but the principles are the same. Higher voltage is more *force* in the flow electricity, and higher current is a larger *rate* of the flow of electricity, as in the amount of total electricity flowing.

Power (wattage)

Once you understand voltage and current, you can use them to determine the power of an electrical supply. Electrical power is measured in watts (W). Watts are a unit of *power*, not energy. This is often confused by beginners, so don't make that mistake. Power is an instantaneous measurement, unlike energy, which is a total quantity. To make another car analogy, power is like the horsepower of the engine while energy is like how much fuel you have in your gas tank. While slamming on the gas pedal you might be using 200 horsepower at that instant, which is irrespective of whether you have 2 liters or 20 liters of gas in your tank.

Electrical power is easy to calculate. The power in watts is simply equal to the voltage in volts multiplied by the current in amps. So if I measure a voltage as 5 V and I measure the current flowing due to that voltage as 2 A, then the total electrical power in that circuit at the moment I measured is 10 W (5 V x 2 A = 10 W). But because power is an instantaneous measurement, that 10 W could easily change. If the current doubles to 4 A instead of 2 A, the new power in that circuit is now 20 W (5 V x 4 A = 20 W).

If we go back to our water analogy, power would be similar to the ability of the hose to fill a pool. Faster filling is like higher power. Notice I said faster *filling*, and not faster *moving* water. That's because power takes into account both the voltage (speed of the water) and the current (width of the hose). So we could fill a pool in equal time by using either a thin garden hose with super high water pressure (high voltage and low current) or a wide fire hose with low water pressure (low voltage and high current). Since power equals volts x amps, increasing either will increase the power, and decreasing either will decrease the power. You can also maintain the same power by increasing one while decreasing the other by the same proportion.

Again, this water analogy isn't exact since electricity is a little more complicated than this, but the analogy works for our purposes. We aren't getting an electrical engineering degree here; we're just trying to understand the basics of electricity.

It is important to note though that when transferring electrical power over a long distance, such as through very long wires, you will lose more power as heat when you have higher current than when you have higher voltage. Higher voltage can be transferred longer distances without as much power loss. That means for the same amount of power (Volts x Amps), it would be better to use higher voltage and lower amps when transferring electricity over long distances, instead of using higher amps and lower volts. This might sound superfluous now, but it will be relevant to us when we start planning for our wires that connect to our solar panels.

Voltage and current are the two most important parameters that must be considered when working with electricity, but they certainly aren't the only parameters. Another concept that you will come across is resistance.

Resistance

Resistance is just like it sounds, it is the resistance against the flow of electricity. This is a normal part of the flow of electricity. All electrical current flowing through a circuit experiences some level of resistance. Keep in mind that resistance is actually a parameter of the *material* that the electricity is flowing through. Resistance is not actually a measure or parameter of the electricity itself. Electricity always flows through a medium, or some pathway, such as a wire, a spring contact, or even your tongue when you licked that 9V battery that I specifically told you not to lick.

Every medium has a different amount of resistance against the flow of electricity. Copper has a very low resistance, which is why it is commonly used in wires. Plastic has an extremely high resistance, which is why it is used on the outside of electrical connectors to shield and protect the connectors from touching anything conductive and causing an electrical short circuit. When the electricity touches the plastic, it won't flow through it because plastic has extremely high resistance. Very low resistance materials, such as copper and other metals, are called conductors, since they conduct electricity well. Very high resistance materials, such as plastic and wood, are known as insulators, since they insulate against the flow of electricity.

If we go back to our water analogy, resistance is something you've probably experienced before. The water that flows out of your faucet probably comes out pretty fast. But if you hooked up a long hose to it, the water will come out slower from the end of the hose. That's because the water experiences significant internal friction in the hose, which is the hose's resistance. Note that this is not the resistance *of the water* in the hose, rather it is the resistance *of the hose* acting on the water.

Now imagine if you hooked up three or four of those hoses end to end, creating a really long hose. The water would come out even slower at the end of the last hose, since now it experiences even more resistance to flow from each successive hose.

Remember the fire hose we talked about earlier? It has a lot less resistance to flow than a thin garden hose because the fire hose is much wider. Therefore, even if you had the same water pressure in both hoses, the water would flow with less resistance in the fire hose, and you'd get higher water flow from it. The same thing applies to electricity. If you have a thin copper wire and thick copper wire, the thin copper wire will have more resistance to the flow of electricity than the thick copper wire, even with the same voltage or electrical force.

Direct Current Vs Alternating Current

Alright, now we know all about voltage, current, and resistance. Those are the most important parameters that you'll need to be familiar with in order to work with electricity. But there's a bit more that must be introduced before I can unleash you into the world of electrical power.

We learned that electricity is simply energy made up of flowing charged particles. In fact, there are actually two types of electricity, and they are distinguished based on the way they flow. These two types of electricity are known as Direct Current and Alternating Current. I'll start with direct current because it's a bit easier to understand, and it fits into our water model better than alternating current.

Direct current, also known as DC, means that the flow of electricity is always in the same direction. Imagine if we had a water pump and we connected one end of a hose to the pump's outlet and the other end of the hose to the pump's inlet. If the hose is filled with water and we turn on the pump, then the water will just keep flowing around in that circle forever, right? We've created one continuous circuit of flowing water.

Now just swap the hose for a wire and the pump for a battery and you go from a water circuit to a DC electrical circuit. (You shouldn't actually do this to a battery though, because this is known as a short circuit, where electricity from the battery flows right back into itself without anything in the way to slow down the flow. This can be dangerous, and you usually want some device in-line to use the electricity before it returns to the battery.)

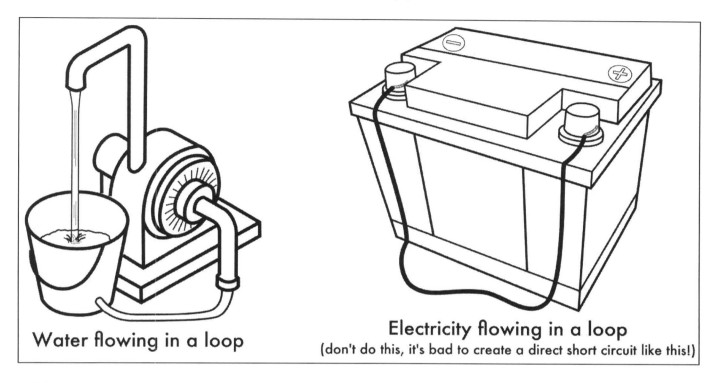

Water flowing in a loop

Electricity flowing in a loop
(don't do this, it's bad to create a direct short circuit like this!)

All batteries are DC devices, meaning they only send current, or the flow of electricity, in one direction, just like the water pump in the example above. It's a one-way street - no going backwards.

Photovoltaics, the solar panels that we'll learn more about in Chapter 3, are also DC devices and only send electricity in one direction.

Batteries and PVs are both power sources, meaning they supply electricity, which is DC electricity in both of these cases. Devices that are designed to be powered by DC electricity can often be connected to batteries or PV panels directly. Whether using a battery or a PV cell as a power supply, current will always flow from the positive terminal of the power supply through the circuit and into the negative terminal of the power supply.

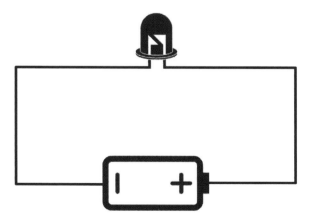

LED connected to a battery in a DC circuit

For example, a simple light emitting diode (LED) is a DC device designed to allow current to flow through it in only one direction. You can connect it directly to a battery or PV cell to supply DC electricity to the LED, provided that you have correctly matched the LED's necessary parameters, such as voltage and current.

However, not all electrical devices use DC electricity. In fact, most of the electrical devices and appliances in your home use Alternating Current, or AC. The outlets in your walls that provide either 110 V or 220 V (depending on the outlet and the country you live in) are AC outlets, meaning they provide AC electricity.

AC electricity flows differently than DC electricity. In an AC circuit, the flow of electricity actually reverses directions many times per second. Unlike in a DC circuit, which is a one-way street, an AC circuit flows both ways, rapidly switching directions. This is achieved by switching the polarity of the electricity, which changes which terminal of the power supply is positive and which is negative. Unlike a battery or PV cell, which has a constant positive and negative terminal, an AC power supply will rapidly switch its positive and negative terminals. This creates a flow of electricity just like in DC, except that the flow reverses and goes the opposite way every few milliseconds.

In the US, electricity in homes is usually 110 VAC at 60 Hz, which means the direction of the flow of electricity switches directions and then switches back 60 times each second. In Europe and much of the rest of the world, the electricity in homes is usually 220 VAC at 50 Hz, meaning the flow of electricity switches directions and switches back 50 times each second.

Many homes in the US will also have a 220 VAC line as well for running more powerful devices such as clothes dryers or ovens.

If you've ever felt like you could see fluorescent light bulbs flickering rapidly, and other people told you that you were crazy, then rest assured - you're not crazy. Or at least, not because of the light thing.

Because the AC current is actually reversing back and forth 50 or 60 times per second, there are actually 100 or 120 instances every second where the current has stopped flowing. These incredibly short pauses mean that the voltage is actually dropping to zero on its way to becoming negative (meaning the current is flowing backwards) before switching and becoming positive, again passing over zero volts on the way back to 110 V or 220 V. These tiny fractions of a second with zero voltage will result in a brief period of the light bulb dimming. If you watch a slow motion video of a light bulb, you will clearly see it briefly dim a hundred or more times per second. This dimming period is sometimes a bit longer with fluorescent bulbs than old fashioned incandescent bulbs, making them easier to spot. However, most people's eyes still aren't acute enough to perceive this incredibly short dimming period, and light bulbs just look constantly 'on' to us.

Here's a bit of fun side trivia: there was once a 'war' that was waged over how electricity would be delivered to our homes. Thomas Edison was a proponent of DC, and envisioned small power stations spread out across cities to create local power sources for nearby communities. On the other hand, Nikola Tesla and George Westinghouse supported AC for transmission of electricity to homes. The AC electricity was intended to be produced by a few larger and more central power stations located further away from the homes using the electricity.

The deciding factor came down to power loss. Long wires stretching for miles have a lot of resistance, and electricity that flows through them loses energy due to heat caused by that resistance. The higher the current, the more power was lost. The solution was to increase the voltage, or electrical pressure, so that the current could be reduced, thus resulting in less power loss. However, over 100 years ago it was much easier to step up the voltage of AC and then drop it back down again once it reaches its destination than it was to do the same for DC. Thus, AC was found to be more efficient for transmitting power over long distances. This ultimately decided the structure of electrical grids all over the world.

That isn't to say that DC isn't useful. In many ways, it is much more useful than AC power due to its simplicity and the ability to use DC power supplies such as PV cells and batteries to directly power devices. However, because our homes use AC power, it is necessary to convert DC into AC if we want to use it to power AC appliances in our home.

This means that if you are making a small solar electricity-powered project, such as a phone charger, electric buggy or simple lighting setup, DC is likely a better option since you can connect devices directly to your power supply. But if you're trying to power your home, you'll need to include a few extra devices that complicate things just a bit. Don't worry though, we'll cover everything you need for both AC and DC projects in the following chapters.

Chapter 3: How solar panels work

Solar panels used for generating electricity are comprised of many individual photovoltaic cells. These PV cells operate using the *photoelectric effect*. The photoelectric effect is a property of materials that absorb photons, which are simply energized light particles, and in return release electrons. A useful electric current is created by capturing these newly flowing electrons in an electrical circuit.

Now hold onto your hat, because we're going to get a little science-y here for a minute while we learn about how these PV cells generate electric current. If you're not into the science and you just want the practical stuff, then don't worry. This will be over shortly.

Today's PV cells are built on a foundation of two silicon wafers. These thin slices of silicon are semiconductors, which are materials that have only moderate conducting properties. They're not as conductive as common metals, but they are still more conductive than common insulators.

The two silicon layers in a PV cell are treated with different chemicals. The first silicon layer, known as the P-type silicon layer, is treated with boron or gallium. These are elements that naturally have one less electron in their outer shells than silicon. The other silicon layer, known as the N-type silicon layer, is treated with a different element, usually phosphorous, which has one more electron in its outer shell compared to silicon.

The boron or gallium want to bond with the silicon in the wafer, but they need an extra electron to complete the bond and become stable. Phosphorous, on the other hand, also wants to bond with silicon, but when it does, it winds up with one extra electron that isn't needed to become stable. That extra electron is not used in the bond between the phosphorous and the silicone, and so it is free to flow around as it pleases.

When the two thin slices of silicon are placed on top of each other, the P-type and N-type wafers come in contact with each other. The extra electrons in the very edge of the N-type wafer flow over into the vacancies where the P-type wafer is missing electrons. This creates a sort of mixing area in the middle known as the *depletion zone*. In the depletion zone, the electrons have moved from the N-type wafer to fill the vacancies in the P-type wafer.

You likely remember from chemistry or physics that electrons are negatively charged particles. Thus, their new presence on the P-type wafer creates negatively charged ions, and their sudden absence on the N-type wafer creates positively charge ions. Now the P-type wafer is negatively charged and the N-type wafer is positively charged.

However, because of the internal electric field that is now created, the P-type wafer doesn't want to accept any more electrons past its depletion zone, since it is already negatively charged and any more electrons would make it even more negatively charged.

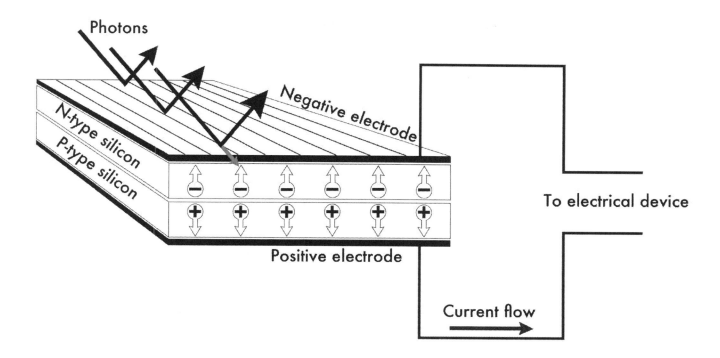

How a photovoltaic cell works

Now here is where sunlight comes in. Rays of sunlight bombard the silicon layers, knocking loose electrons and creating new electron vacancies in their place. Because of the oppositely charged sides of the silicon wafers, the electrons only flow one way. By attaching a wire or other conductor to the two sides of the silicon wafers (in reality this is usually an aluminum plate), we can create a pathway for the electrons to move. That creates a current flow that we can exploit to power electrical devices.

And therein lies the magic of how PV cells can generate electricity from the sun. Each photon that knocks loose an electron causes it to get pushed through the terminals and the circuit of any device connected to the PV cell, until the electron works its way back around into the other side of the silicon wafer. At that point, the process repeats all over again when the electrons fill in the vacancies in the silicon wafers left by recently departed electrons. So I guess it isn't magic after all, it's science!

Simple PV circuits

It is important to note that when we talk about the electricity generated by PV cells, we are talking about direct current (DC). We know this is direct current because it's only flowing one way around the circuit in a continuous loop. Anytime you see the voltage of a PV cell or panel you should know that it is always DC voltage, not AC voltage. The specifications might only list it as 12 V and not specifically as 12 VDC, but you should know that we're always talking about DC when we're dealing with electricity generated by PV cells.

Each PV cell can only create a voltage difference of approximately 0.5 - 0.6 V between the two silicon wafers, depending on how ideal the conditions are. That's not much voltage. A little AA battery for a flashlight has a voltage of closer to 1.5 V, which is three times as much as a PV cell.

For calculations, I often use 0.5 V as the voltage of a PV cell instead of 0.6 V. In reality, it can be a few tenths of a volt higher, but using 0.5 V helps with easier mental math. When you're doing exact calculations, you can use more exact figures, but also know that the voltage will vary a small amount anyways depending on conditions.

Even though 0.5 V is a very low voltage, we can easily achieve higher voltages from PV cells by simply connecting them in series, which is where a positive terminal is connected to the next cell's negative terminal. Multiple PV cells connected in series is known as a module. If we connect the positive terminal of one PV cell to the negative terminal of another, we can create a module with double the voltage of a single PV cell. This is how series connections work. If we add a third PV cell in series, the module will have three times the original voltage, or 1.5 V.

Most common 12 V solar panel modules use sets of 36 cells in series. This gives an open circuit voltage of approximately 18 V (when measured at the terminals without a load). However, when you add a load, such as a light bulb, battery charger or any other device, the voltage drops somewhat, approaching a value closer to the useful 12 V that many DC devices require.

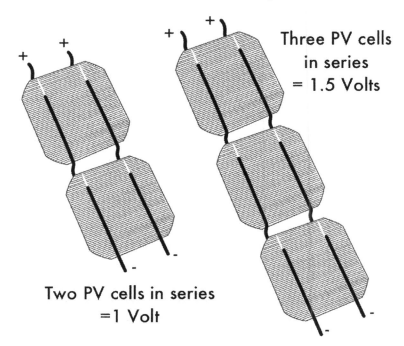

Three PV cells
in series
= 1.5 Volts

Two PV cells in series
=1 Volt

Smaller devices that only require 5 V to charge, such as cell phones and other USB devices, can be powered with just 12 cells in series.

The current produced by a PV cell depends on its size. With more surface area to capture more sunlight, a larger PV cell can produce higher current. No matter the size though, all PV cells still produce around 0.5 V. Increasing the size effectively increases the power, measured in watts, as watts are simply calculated by multiplying voltage by current. Thus, increasing the current also increases the power.

Another way to increase the current of a PV module, other than simply buying larger PV cells, is to connect multiple PV cells in parallel. A parallel connection is created by connecting the positive terminals of multiple PV cells together on one side, and the negative terminals of the cells together on the other. Parallel connections increase the current but leave the voltage unchanged. This is the opposite of series connections, which increase the voltage but leave the current unchanged.

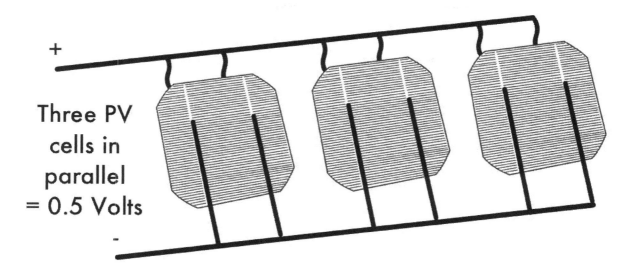

Three PV cells in parallel = 0.5 Volts

So for example, if we have three PV cells that are each rated for 1 A and 0.5 V, we could put them in parallel to create a module that outputs 3 A and 0.5 V. That gives us three times the current (and thus three times the power) of the original single PV cell, while maintaining the same voltage that we started with.

We can also easily calculate the wattage of this module by multiplying the final current (3 A) by the final voltage (0.5 V) to give us 1.5 watts. Not much, but it's a start!

And why stop there? Since we already understand how series and parallel connections work, let's build an even bigger imaginary PV module. Let's take those three PV cells that we wired in parallel for example. That's a 3 A and 0.5 V module. We can use it to create higher voltage that can be useful for powering something more realistic. If we want to build a 12 V panel, we'll need to generate closer to 18 V in reality. So let's make another 35 of those three-cell parallel modules. With 36 of those modules total, we can wire them all in series now, and create a larger module that outputs 18 V and 3 A at open circuit. With a load, that voltage will sag lower, making it effective for a 12 V setup.

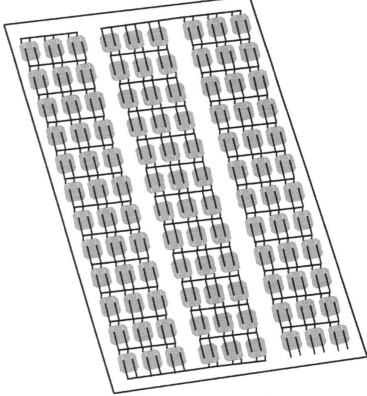

36 modules in series of the three-parallel cells = 18 Volts

Now here's a little secret of the solar industry - you never really get as many watts as the panel is rated for. A solar panel sold as a "100 W panel" will never actually give you 100 watts. That's because the manufacturers rate their panels based on the open circuit voltage. So for our module above, we can calculate the open circuit power as 18 V x 3 A = 54 W. But in reality, since our voltage will drop, we'll really be getting something closer to maybe 13 V or 14 V during use. That means we'd get a usable 39-42 W from this panel. Doesn't sound as good as 54 W, does it? That's why the manufacturers prefer to list the open circuit power and not the real world power. Just keep it in mind that if you need a realistic 70 W, you better aim for at least a 100 W panel, just to be safe.

Applications of solar panel systems

So now you know how PV cells work and how they can be combined to create enough voltage and current to power electronic devices. At this point, it is time to learn how to create useful circuits from our new solar panels.

There are a number of ways to accomplish this:

- Small scale DC solar electricity (mostly table top projects)
- Large scale AC solar electricity (in off-grid installations)
- Hybrid AC/DC solar electricity (in off-grid installations)
- Grid-tie solar electricity (grid connected)

We'll cover each one of these individually in the following sections.

Small scale DC solar projects

Small scale DC solar projects are the easiest types of solar electricity projects. If you've never played with solar power before, this is where I recommend you start.

For DC projects, we don't need to worry about inverting DC electricity into AC electricity. Instead, we'll only be powering DC devices, since they use the same DC electricity generated by the solar panel.

Imagine that we have a simple 12 V solar panel rated for 10 W. This should be about the size of a sheet of notebook paper. Since it creates 12 VDC electricity, theoretically we could plug it directly into a device that is rated for 12 VDC, such as as a 12 VDC light bulb or string of light bulbs. However, the power supplied by a solar panel isn't always constant. It changes based on the amount of sun the panel is receiving, which can be affected by everything from cloud cover to the changing angle of the sun overhead. Because of this variable power, many DC devices won't work well if directly connected to a solar panel. This is especially true for more sensitive electronics. Simpler electronics, like a heater or an electric motor, can handle variable power better. It usually won't damage the device; it will just mean the heater won't work as quickly or the motor won't spin as powerfully.

However, because many DC devices need more stable power, it is much more common to use another device, known as a charge controller, together with a battery, in between the PV cell module and the load. This helps regulate the voltage and provide a stable power supply to the device.

With this setup, you'll need a minimum of four devices:

- A solar panel
- A charge controller
- A rechargeable battery
- A DC device for the load

A solar charge controller is a device that receives electricity from the solar panel, regulates that electricity to a stable and appropriate voltage, and then outputs it to a battery. This effectively charges the battery and stores the energy for later use. Some charge controllers also allow you to connect a load directly to the charge controller, bypassing the battery altogether. Charging a battery is only around 90-95% efficient in most cases, and so if you need the power immediately, it can be more efficient to use it directly from the source rather than lose 5-10% en route to storage (the battery), then take it back out of storage later with another efficiency loss.

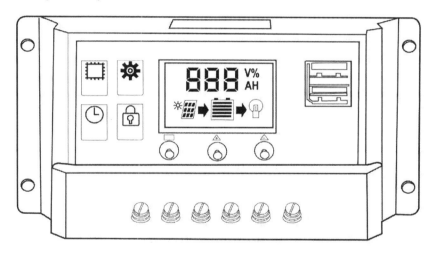

An example of a typical low power charge controller

There are many different styles and power levels of charge controllers out there, but there are only two main types: Pulse Width Modulation (PWM) and Maximum Power Point Tracking (MPPT).

PWM charge controllers are the simpler and cheaper of the two, but they are somewhat less efficient. Like all charge controllers, as the battery gets closer to being fully charged, it slowly decreases the amount of power going to the battery. This is better for long term battery health.

MPPT charge controllers perform a similar function, but they are smarter, allowing them to take excess voltage and turn it into additional power. This can speed up the charging of a battery in the early stage of battery charging. MPPT charge controllers are thus more efficient because they can continuously adjust the charging parameters to achieve the maximum amount of power from the solar panel, instead of letting some of it go to waste, as PWM charge controllers do.

Another advantage of MPPT charge controllers is that they can accept a much higher input voltage than the battery requires. With a PWM charge controller connected to a 12 V battery, you can't provide much more than 24 V from the solar panel. There are a few PWM charge controllers designed to take higher voltage, but they end up just wasting that excess voltage. On the other hand, you can deliver higher voltage to most MPPT charge controllers, even when charging a lower 12 V battery, since the MPPT charge controller is smart enough to convert any extra voltage into extra current. This results in higher power and higher efficiency.

For small scale hobby projects, it's often not worth the extra cost of an MPPT charge controller. The difference in efficiency is small enough that it would take years or even decades to recoup the cost of an MPPT charge controller, meaning PWM charge controllers are just fine for most types of small scale projects. For large scale solar power projects, especially those powering an entire home, an MPPT charge controller can quickly recoup the higher cost due to increased efficiency in a high power system. We'll talk more about MPPT charge controllers later in the chapter, as they are more relevant for larger projects.

For a small scale DC project, we've already discussed solar panels and charge controllers. Now we need a battery. The sun only shines for part of the day, so if we want to save the energy we are generating during the day for later at night or when it is cloudy, we will need some way to store it. Our battery can store the energy generated by the solar panels and allow us to hang onto it for days, weeks or even years.

This is still an overview chapter showing how different solar setups work, so we'll save the specifics of battery selection for Chapter 4. But don't worry, we'll dive in fairly deep there, so any battery nerds like me out there won't be left out!

The last thing we'll need for our small DC solar system is a load. This is any device that can be powered by DC voltage. Specifically, it should be able to operate using the DC voltage provided by our battery. This means that if we have a 12 V battery, we can't run a 5 V cell phone charger from the battery directly. However, we can always include a DC-DC converter in-line to convert the 12 VDC down to 5 VDC.

A typical small scale solar DC setup will look like this. The solar panel plugs directly into the charge controller, which itself plugs into the battery. Lastly, the 12 V device connects to the battery to receive power.

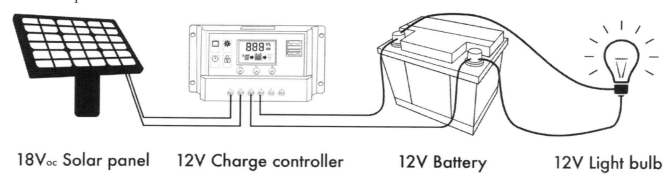

18V$_{oc}$ Solar panel   12V Charge controller   12V Battery   12V Light bulb

This is the basic setup, but it can be altered and adjusted to create nearly anything. As mentioned earlier, we could add a 12 V to 5 V DC-DC converter and use this setup to charge USB devices like cell phones and tablets simply by replacing the light bulb in the diagram above with a 5 VDC USB charger. We could swap out the light bulb for a fan and bring this setup camping or to the beach on hot days. We could use it to power a 12 V pump for irrigating crops in an area that is too far away to run an extension cord. We could add a motion activated camera and place this system outside of a hunting stand or cabin to see what kind of wildlife comes wandering through the area. Our load could be a higher powered battery charger for charging an electric bicycle. Or we could power a drivetrain directly by connecting a 12 V electric outrigger motor and mounting it on a canoe or kayak to make an electric boat.

The possibilities are truly endless! If it can run on DC power, you can power it with a simple DC solar setup just like this. We'll talk more about the specifics of building these types of setups in Chapter 6, which covers small scale solar projects like these in more detail.

Large scale AC solar projects (off-grid)

The principles for small scale DC projects that we learned about from the previous few pages can also be applied on a larger scale to power an entire house. However, we're going to need to go through an additional step to invert our electricity from DC into AC, which is the type of electricity used in homes.

In this section, we'll be looking at a general overview of an "off-grid" solar power system. Off-grid simply means that the system is standalone and not connected to the local municipal power grid. Instead of being connected to the grid and being able to also draw power from the grid when necessary, an off-grid setup requires its own energy storage solution in the form of batteries to ensure that it always has enough stored energy available to meet the household demand (or it will require a gasoline or diesel generator to charge the batteries during extended periods without sun). Grid-connected systems on the other hand, more commonly known as grid-tied systems, are a different can of worms and we will cover them shortly.

The beginning of an off-grid home setup is the same as in small scale DC projects. We'll need to start with the solar panels, but in this case, we'll need more than we used for small scale DC projects. In fact, we'll likely need a *lot* more. Some homes have small solar arrays of just a few hundred watts that are used for only a fraction of the home's energy needs. Other homes have arrays of a few thousands or even tens of thousands of watts that can provide all the electricity necessary to power the home, often creating a surplus.

The solar panels will connect to a charge controller, though this will be a much larger charge controller than the ones covered in the previous section. The charge controller must be robust enough to handle many hundreds or thousands of watts.

The charge controller will be connected to the battery to receive and store energy. This will be a much larger battery or group of batteries than the ones we talked about using in the previous section for small-scale DC projects, but we'll cover battery specifics in detail in Chapter 4. For now, suffice it to say that we're talking about a big battery pack for a standard size home.

Next, the battery is connected to an AC inverter. The purpose of the AC inverter is to take the DC electricity supplied by the battery and invert it into AC electricity, which the house requires. This is usually 110 VAC in the USA and 220 VAC in most of the rest of the world, except for a few random countries (Japan, Colombia, most of the Caribbean islands and a few other random countries, I'm looking at you!).

AC inverters come in all sizes and price ranges. Generally, the more power they can handle, the more expensive they will be. There are also two types of AC inverters, pure-sine wave AC inverters and non-sine wave AC inverters (also known as square wave AC inverters). If the inverter doesn't say which type it is, then it's almost certainly a non-sine wave inverter. Cheaper non-sine wave inverters are fine for some devices, but anything with sensitive electronics like a TV or computer requires the cleaner electrical signal that a pure-sine wave inverter provides.

A popular high-power inverter

Next we have the AC breaker box, which is connected to the inverter. The inverter feeds AC electricity into the breaker box in your home, where it can then be distributed to different circuits throughout your home. There are also circuit breakers in the box that correspond to each circuit. These circuit breakers will "blow" or switch off if you try to pull too much power through a single circuit, such as if you try to use your welder while blow drying your hair and microwaving popcorn all at the same time.

An AC breaker box is a crucial step in creating an off-grid home, and it must not be skipped. Unlike small scale DC solar projects, the AC electricity in your home can easily cause property damage or death if not handled correctly. A properly installed AC breaker box is a necessity. Unless you are a professional or at least have considerable home wiring experience, this shouldn't be attempted alone. It is recommended to have a professional help you install it. In some areas, it is illegal to do this work by yourself, as only licensed professionals are permitted to install AC circuitry in homes. Check your local laws and make sure you don't work afoul of them. A DC battery can shock you, but AC can kill with just 10% of the lethal current required by DC.

Lastly, the AC breaker box feeds into the different circuits spread around a home. These circuits are often divided by room, though many larger rooms will have multiple circuits. There can be a number of AC electrical outlets on a single circuit, all drawing power from the same source and sharing a single electrical breaker switch in the AC breaker box.

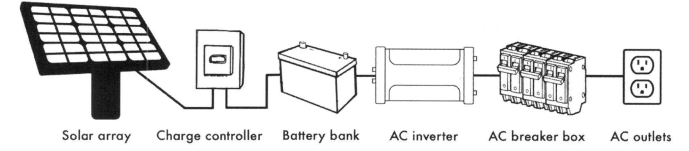

Solar array   Charge controller   Battery bank   AC inverter   AC breaker box   AC outlets

Note: this is a simplified diagram and doesn't include extra safety components such as fuses and cut-off switches

In addition to the electrical components listed above, many off-grid setups will keep a gasoline or diesel generator on hand. If the batteries are getting low after heavier than normal use, or there has been less intense sun than normal, a generator may be required to recharge the batteries, as there is no municipal backup power in an off-grid installation.

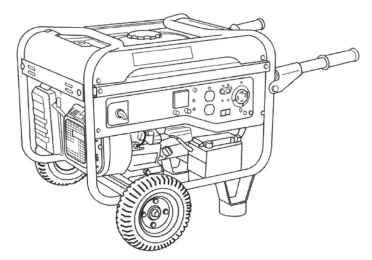

A high power battery charger will be connected to the generator to quickly recharge the batteries and minimize the time that the generator must run. It is best to build a sufficiently large solar setup to avoid using a generator often, but it is a useful tool to have during times of unpredictable use or extended periods of poor weather.

Hybrid AC & DC solar electricity (off-grid)

In some cases, you might want to have both an AC electrical circuit and a DC electrical circuit installed in your home. This can be a more efficient setup depending what devices you need to power.

A good example is a medium sized installation, such as for a vacation or hunting cabin. Since these are often far off the beaten path, it can be expensive to run electrical lines from the power company. A cheaper method is to install a solar power setup. However, because these are often smaller buildings and not used 24/7, they can take advantage of a smaller hybrid setup.

Using DC power directly from the battery without needing an inverter to convert to AC is more efficient. Small, efficient 12 VDC lighting can be installed in cabins to reduce energy consumption. A DC well pump can be powered when running water is required. There are even 12 VDC refrigerators that can be powered only when the cabin is in use.

Of course, there are many devices that might still require AC electricity, such as televisions, kitchen appliances, etc. To power these, an AC inverter can be connected to the battery and a few AC appliances can be plugged directly into the inverter.

The setup described above would include mostly DC appliances, with an AC inverter that is available to directly power a handful of AC appliances. However, you could also do the opposite, and build a predominantly AC system that also has some DC use. This would be great for an off-grid home that desires to become more efficient by charging devices directly off of DC, despite running most home appliances and devices from AC.

Any device you own that has a battery will also use a DC charger. This includes many devices such as cell phones, laptops, tablets, e-readers, toys, robotic vacuums, electric toothbrushes and razors, bluetooth speakers, portable battery banks, etc. To charge these devices, you usually plug the charger into the wall outlet, right? So the charger is taking that AC electricity and converting it into DC to charge the battery in your device.

But wait, remember that your solar power system starts off as DC! So in effect, you're creating DC electricity from your solar panels, converting it to AC with an inverter to send it into your home's outlets, then your charger is turning it *back* into DC for your device. That's a lot of wasted energy in each conversion. It is much more efficient to use the DC electricity directly.

This can often be achieved directly from the charge controller, before the electricity from your solar panel ever makes it to the battery for storage. Many charge controllers have load outlets, whether they are a few 5 VDC USB outlets on small charge controllers or a dedicated 12 VDC socket on larger charge controllers. If your charge controller doesn't have a load outlet, you can still connect directly to your 12 V battery to power 12 VDC devices. In effect, you're taking some of that DC electricity in your battery and using it closer to the source, before it reaches your AC inverter.

Be warned though: if you tap directly into your battery (or even to your charge controller's load outlet) then you still have to make sure that you are matching the correct voltage for your device.

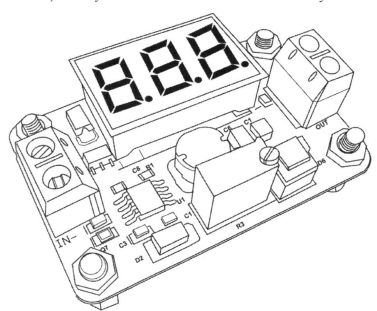

Typical DC-DC voltage converter

Check the wall charger's data sticker to determine the DC output voltage. USB devices generally require 5 VDC, but some, especially those charging on the USB C protocol, can use higher voltages. Non-USB devices like electric razors or other battery devices might require odd voltages like 3 VDC or 9 VDC.

No matter the voltage, you can use a DC-DC converter to obtain it. Some DC-DC converters are adjustable, while others are fixed, such as a 12 V to 5 V DC-DC converter. Simply choose the correct voltage for your device and make sure it is rated to handle the current (or power) that your device requires, which should also be listed on the charger's data sticker.

Grid-tied solar electricity systems

A grid-tied setup is a common method for powering homes. Unlike an off-grid solar power system, grid-tied systems remain connected to the local electrical grid in your town. Grid-tied setups have one major advantage over off-grid setups - they don't require any local energy storage. That means you can save a lot of money by not needing to buy an expensive battery bank.

The principle of a grid-tied system is that it generates much or all of the electricity needed by the house during the day, but still takes energy from the electrical grid at night when the sun isn't shining.

This might seem like it only solves half the problem - why install a solar electricity system if you can only use it during the day and still depend on the local electrical grid at night? The answer is called *net-metering*.

Net-metering is the practice of allowing electricity to flow both ways, both from the electrical grid to your home (like normal) and also from your home back into the electrical grid. If you install enough solar panels to create an excess amount of electricity, net metering allows your excess electricity to flow back into the grid to the electric company. In essence, your meter spins backwards anytime you are generating more electricity than you're using.

With net-metering, if you can generate electricity for just 8 hours a day, but you generate three times as much energy as you use during those 8 hours, then you'll effectively be getting free energy back from the electrical company during the other 16 hours. This gives you the benefit of not paying the electrical company for electricity anymore and not having to buy expensive batteries.

Of course, grid-tied systems aren't without their drawbacks. First of all, if you thought that net-metering sounded too good to be true, then you might be right. Thanks to lobbying by the electrical companies, some areas have begun outlawing it. In other areas, power companies are only required to credit you a fraction of the cost of electricity, not the full amount of what most people pay for the same amount of electricity. You'll have to research your local laws to determine if net-metering is used in your area and what restrictions may apply.

Secondly, being grid-tied means you're still dependent on the electrical grid for power when the sun isn't shining. If the power ever goes out due to a storm or any other reason, you'll have electricity during the day, but as soon as the sun starts to disappear, so does your electricity. Sure, you can get around with flashlights, but your fridge isn't going to stay cold and your AC is just going to be an expensive network of copper pipes until the sun comes back up in the morning. And if it was a big storm that knocked out your local electrical grid, you're probably not going to have much sun even in the daytime until the storm passes.

For this reason, some people with grid-tied systems will keep a small backup battery charged that they can use for essentials when both the power and the sun go out.

The last downside is that grid-tied systems can be a bit more complicated to setup, and many areas require that a licensed professional do the installation work, or at the very least sign off on it. However, even if you don't have laws requiring a professional to check your grid-tied system out, it is still *highly* recommended to pay someone to inspect your work anyways. Again, AC can kill. Don't mess around with it unless you are properly trained.

Grid-tied systems have to properly integrate with the electrical company's grid infrastructure. This involves connecting to the electricity meter and also having some type of shutoff switch to break the connection to the grid in case the power goes out. If power is down everywhere, you don't want your solar panels to be feeding electricity to the whole neighborhood, do you? There are options for automatic cut-off switches that know when the power suddenly goes out and can automatically disconnect your home from the grid. At the very least though, you'll want a manual switch you can flip in the event of an emergency, just like the cut-off valves for water or natural gas lines that enter your home.

Additionally, many areas require that the grid-tie system includes an automatic shutoff, often in the grid-tie inverter. This is to protect any electrical workers that are operating on the grid during an electricity outage.

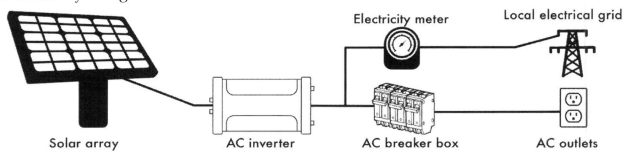

Note: this is a simplified diagram and doesn't include extra safety components such as fuses and cut-off switches

Chapter 4: Batteries

Note: Batteries contain a large amount of energy and can be dangerous if you don't know what you're doing. Please be careful and don't attempt anything that you are not trained to handle.

If you plan to build a solar powered installation or small project that requires storing solar energy for use at another time, particularly when the sun isn't shining, then you'll need to use batteries.

Batteries are an integral part of building solar power setups for that very reason, they give you much more flexibility in how and when you use the energy that your solar panels worked so hard to create.

However, not all batteries are created equally. When it comes to storing power, there are two main battery options that have very different characteristics: lead acid based batteries and lithium-ion batteries. One is not necessarily better than the other, as each have their own unique advantages and disadvantages. The choice for you mostly comes down to what your specific project requires.

Let's take a look at both types of batteries to learn which is better for different types of applications. We'll start with lead acid batteries.

Lead acid batteries

Lead acid batteries are one of the oldest battery technologies still in use today. They are commonly found in car batteries, golf carts, marine and boat batteries and off-grid home energy storage battery banks, though lithium-ion batteries are quickly eating into the market share of lead acid batteries home energy storage use as well.

Lead acid batteries, as the name implies, are made of lead and acid. To put it simply, the battery consists of lead plates bathing in an electrolyte solution of water and sulfuric acid. Individual lead acid battery cells have a voltage of approximately 2.0 V, but it is more difficult to find single cells. It is much more common for multiple cells to be included in a single battery. The most common configuration for lead acid batteries are three cells in series to create 6 V batteries or six cells in series to create 12 V batteries. You can also find 24 V batteries, but it is more common to just wire two 12 V batteries in series to create a 24 V lead acid battery pack.

Some lead acid batteries are sealed, meaning the entire battery is enclosed in a water-tight plastic case. These are known as Sealed Lead Acid batteries, or SLAs for short. Sealed lead acids are safer because you can knock them around and flip them upside down without spilling acid everywhere. Other lead acid batteries, known as wet cell lead acid batteries or flooded lead acid batteries, have an acid bath that is not sealed. Wet cell or flooded lead acid batteries should never be turned on their sides or upside down, as the acid can easily leak out.

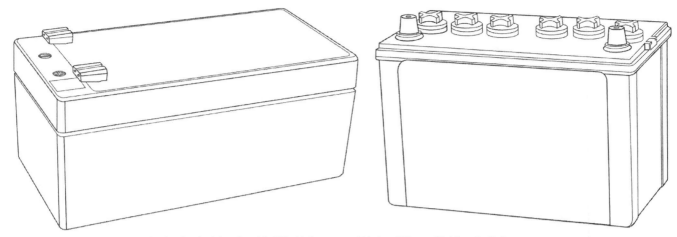

Left: Sealed lead acid (SLA) battery; Right: Wet-cell (flooded) battery

Sealed lead acid batteries are more convenient to use because they require no maintenance or caution when moving them. You just plug them in and forget about them. However, they don't last as long as wet-cell lead acid batteries. Wet-cells last longer, but this comes at a price. They are both more expensive and require more maintenance. It is important to check the acid level inside the cells regularly and top them off as the water slowly evaporates. Also, they require some ventilation due to the evaporation. Lastly, they don't handle extreme temperature ranges as well because the water can either freeze or evaporate more quickly, depending on the weather.

Sealed lead acid batteries are better suited for projects that require the battery to be in motion, such as in a vehicle or a backpack. Wet-cell lead acid batteries are better for stationary batteries, such as for a large powerbank for a building.

Most lead acid batteries are not meant to be discharged completely. A lead acid battery that is rated for 200 charge cycles might die after just a few dozen cycles if it is discharged to 0% each time it is used. Most lead acid manufacturers recommend not discharging more than 50% of the battery capacity. However, deep cycle lead acid batteries exist that can be discharged through as much as 80% of their total capacity, but you'll pay more for those.

Lithium-ion batteries

Unlike the old technology in lead acid batteries, which was developed around 150 years ago, lithium-ion batteries were invented around 40 years ago and only became commercially viable around 20 years ago.

Their production is more complicated than lead acid batteries and requires much more precise tolerances. The cells are made from multiple thin layers of graphite and other materials that vary depending on the type of lithium ion cell, with a thin separator between each layer. The multiple layers are then surrounded by an electrolyte, usually in gel form, that allows lithium ions to move around between the layers. When connected to a circuit, the voltage difference between the terminals in a lithium-ion cell causes electrons to flow through the circuit.

Lithium-ion batteries can be divided into three main groups based on their chemistries. There are in fact dozens, perhaps hundreds of slightly different chemistries used in different types of lithium-ion batteries, but these are the main three categories in which all of those different lithium-ion flavors fall:

Lithium Iron Phosphate (LiFePO4): The heaviest of the lithium battery family, these cells are also the longest lasting and the safest. Most can last for many thousands of cycles. They have a much higher thermal runaway temperature and are less volatile, making it difficult for them to catch on fire. LiFePO4 cells have nominal voltages of approximately 3.2 V, meaning they are lower voltage than other lithium-ion batteries. This nominal voltage makes them easier than other types of lithium-ion batteries to use in 12 V systems, as increments of four cells in series creates batteries in increments of 12.8 V, which is very close to 12 V.

Lithium Polymer (Lipo): A quick history lesson: true "lithium polymer" battery cells don't really exist commercially, at least not yet. They were developed in the lab and used a solid polymer electrolyte instead of a wet gel electrolyte. This made them safer, but also made them harder to use outside of laboratory conditions. They never succeeded commercially. However, people took the name and started using it to describe what are actually called "pouch cells", or lithium-ion battery cells that are enclosed in what looks like a pouch made of aluminum foil. Further still, this term "lipo" began to be used to describe pouch cells that are used in the high power batteries of remote controlled RC toys, airplanes, drones and other small, high power hobby devices. This is the most common use of the term now, and so I will refer to these batteries as "RC lipo", even though this isn't the true, original definition of a lithium polymer battery.

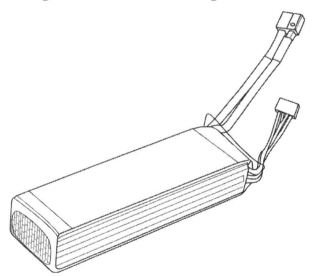

RC lipo batteries are a type of li-ion battery that are capable of much higher power levels. This also makes them much more volatile and dangerous. During normal use, they aren't likely to cause any problem, but if accidentally overcharged or punctured, they can catch on fire and explode. These batteries can not handle any abuse. They are not meant for most handheld projects. Their only common use is for hobby toys, especially flying ones like drones and planes, where extremely high power-to-weight ratios are required. RC lipo batteries can be used in small DC solar projects, but they are not necessarily the best option due to their increased safety risks. Their nominal voltage of 3.7 V is similar to that of the li-ion cells described next.

Lithium-ion (Li-ion): This name is a bit confusing, since technically all three of these chemistries use lithium ions as the mechanism for creating charge. However, this group essentially includes all batteries that aren't RC lipo or LiFePO4. This includes many subtypes of lithium-ion batteries, such as Lithium Nickel Cobalt batteries, Lithium Manganese batteries, Lithium Cobalt Aluminum batteries and dozens of other variations. Li-ion cells usually have a nominal voltage of between 3.6 to 3.7 V.

Together with LiFePO$_4$ batteries, they are the most common lithium batteries used for solar projects. Li-ion cells also come in the widest variety of shapes and sizes, giving much more freedom to custom battery builders. LiFePO$_4$ batteries, on the other hand, come in fewer sizes and varieties, limiting the customizability of battery packs as compared to Li-ion alternatives.

We'll discuss building custom batteries further in this chapter. However, if you want to go deeper and learn everything there is to know about building custom lithium-ion battery packs, I recommend checking out my book *DIY Lithium Batteries: How to Build Your Own Battery Packs*, which is available on Amazon. The entire book focuses purely on building custom battery packs, so it goes into much more detail than I can cover in a single chapter here.

Choosing the battery type for your project

Lead acid and lithium-ion batteries have different advantages and disadvantages. This means that while lead acid batteries might be better for one project, lithium-ion batteries could be a better choice for another project. The advantages and disadvantages of each type are described below to help you determine which is best for your application.

Regardless of the type of lead acid battery used, SLA or wet cell, they all have fairly similar advantages. Lead acid batteries are usually the cheapest type of storage battery available. Different models have comparatively higher or lower costs, mostly related to their lifespans, but they are almost all generally cheaper than lithium-ion batteries. This makes it easier to invest in a larger battery bank when you begin a large solar installation, such as for an off-grid home.

The main disadvantages of lead acid batteries are their comparatively shorter lifespans, lower deep-discharge abilities and heavier weights, as compared to lithium-ion batteries.

Even though there is a large range of lifespans for different types of lead acid batteries, most will die much sooner than lithium-ion batteries, often three to five times as quickly. As mentioned above, most lead acid batteries don't like to be discharged by more than 50% of their capacity. When they are drained below 50% capacity, they undergo a parasitic chemical reaction known as *sulfation* that drastically reduces the life of the battery, requiring a costly replacement sooner. Deep cycle lead acid batteries are more resistant to sulfation, but still can't be discharged completely without damaging them.

Lithium-ion batteries, on the other hand, are much more tolerant of being completely discharged, though it is still healthier to perform only partial discharges when possible. Head to head, lithium-ion batteries can last more than 10 times longer than lead acid batteries when both are discharged completely on a regular basis. But again, you shouldn't be fully discharging lead acid batteries on a regular basis. Lastly, lead acid batteries are much larger and heavier than lithium batteries. A standard 12 V SLA battery is between three to six times heavier and takes up nearly three times the volume compared to a lithium-ion battery of the same capacity.

Furthermore, lead acid batteries don't charge as efficiently as lithium-ion batteries. As much as 15% of the energy used to charge a lead acid battery never actually makes in into storage in the battery. Lithium-ion batteries, on the other hand, lose very little energy when charging.

Compared to lead acid batteries, lithium-ion batteries are lighter, smaller, last longer, are more efficient and can provide more energy without damaging themselves. What's not to like!? Well, lithium-ion batteries do of course come with a few disadvantages.

First of all, they can be much more expensive than lead acid batteries, often three or four times the price. However, if the batteries are intended to be used long term, then lithium-ion batteries can often be cheaper in the long run. Even if they cost four times as much as lead acid batteries, they can often last five times as long or more, meaning you'd spend more by replacing lead acid batteries than if you'd just bought lithium-ion batteries to begin with.

Also, lithium-ion batteries can be more dangerous than lead acid batteries. The stored energy in a lithium-ion battery is more volatile than in a lead acid battery. If a lithium-ion battery is punctured, it can sometimes catch on fire or even explode. Also, if lithium-ion batteries reach extremely high temperatures, usually above 150 °C, they can begin thermal runaway. During thermal runaway, the cell begins to combust and will usually explode violently.

This shouldn't scare you off from lithium-ion batteries. In fact, I almost exclusively use only lithium-ion batteries. When purchased from responsible manufacturers using proper production techniques and when installed properly, they can be incredibly safe. A fire is a rare occurrence often caused by misuse, and large lithium battery arrays usually take safety steps to prevent this, such as active cooling and multiple fuses at different levels, but it is important to know that these things can happen, no matter how rare they are. Wet-cell lead acid batteries aren't inherently safe either with their non-sealed pools of acid and leaking hydrogen gas, but at least they aren't likely to catch on fire.

To quickly summarize, lead acid batteries are cheaper, but also bigger, heavier, less efficient and die quicker. Lithium-ion batteries are more expensive, but are smaller, lighter, more efficient, last longer and can actually be cheaper than lead acid batteries in the long run.

So how do you know which kind to use for your project? The best method is to determine which parameters are more important for your needs.

For example, let's say we are working on a solar powered backpack-mounted charger for cell phones and other USB devices. This is an example of a small scale DC solar project. For this application, we'd mount a solar panel on a backpack and include a small battery for storing the energy during the day. We could use either lithium-ion batteries or lead acid batteries to store the energy. Realistically, we probably won't take advantage of the hundreds or even thousands of cycles that a lithium-ion battery is rated for, unless we are hiking with this thing every weekend for decades, so a lead acid battery, despite having a shorter lifespan, could still be a good option.

If we went that route with a lead acid battery, we'd want to use a sealed lead acid battery so we don't spill acid inside of our backpack. However, that SLA battery is going to be really heavy, maybe even five times as heavy as a lithium-ion battery. So even though both will work, the choice in this case mostly comes down to which is more important: saving money by buying a cheaper SLA battery, or saving weight and space in the bag by buying a more expensive lithium battery?

As you can see, depending on the available budget and preferences, two different people building this exact same project could choose opposite answers to the question "which battery is better?".

Other cases can end up with similar decisions to be made. Take the example of an off-grid family home. In this case, we would need a really large battery bank. The average home in the US uses 30 kWh of electricity per day. Ideally we'd want to build a battery that could hold more than just one day's worth of electricity, so let's say we'll need a 40 kWh battery bank. We're also expecting to use these batteries for a long time, at least the life of the battery pack. Let's plan for 10 years. Space isn't really an issue, so the fact that lithium-ion batteries are smaller and lighter doesn't help us too much. Most people can stash batteries in their basement, shed, garage, etc.

Let's also look at lifespan and cost. If I go to wholesalesolar.com, I can compare lithium-ion batteries and deep cycle lead acid batteries meant for solar setups like ours. A 9.8 kWh RESU10H lithium-ion battery made by LG Chem costs $6,275 at the time this book was published (2018), and we'll need four of those to get close to 40 kWh, so that's a total cost of $25,100, not including shipping or installation costs. On the same site, I can also see that a Crown 2CRP1400, 1000 Ah 2 V flooded lead acid battery costs $655. Because this is a lead acid battery, we really shouldn't discharge it more than 50% for best cycle life, but let's go nuts anyways and push it to 80%. That means to have a usable 40 kWh, we'll need something closer to 48 kWh. Since these are 2 V cells, we'll need to connect 24 cells in series to get enough capacity (and fit nicely with my 48 V devices such as our inverter). That brings the total cost up to $15,720 before installation and shipping costs. So even with 20% more battery, the lead acid batteries are $9,380 cheaper.

However, we also need to consider longevity. The LG Chem lithium batteries come with a 10-year warranty, and are rated to retain 80% of their charge after 10 years. The Crown lead acid batteries only have a 5-year warranty, and their rated capacity after 5 years isn't listed, but it's definitely going to be less than 80% capacity. So if we assume that we'd need to buy another set of Crown lead acid batteries after 5 years, then the total cost of the lead acid batteries after 10 years is $31,440, which is $6,340 more expensive than the lithium-ion batteries after 10 years, not even including the fact that we'd have to pay for shipping twice on those insanely heavy lead acid batteries (3,264 lbs or 1,484 kg). Not only are the lead acid batteries more expensive, but they'll require routine maintenance to monitor their acid levels and they won't charge as efficiently so we won't be able to store as much of our energy as we could with lithium-ion batteries.

Therefore, in this case it becomes pretty clear that lithium-ion batteries are actually a better solution for this imaginary off-grid home that we're building, assuming we have the cash to front in the beginning. Many people prefer to start off small and increase the size of their solar setup over time. In such a case, lead acid batteries can be a cheaper way to begin storing solar power, and in a few years when a larger budget is available and the lead acid batteries have deteriorated, they can then be replaced with lithium-ion batteries.

In essence, the decision between lead acid and lithium-ion batteries all depends on you and your project. Of course, this is only one of the decisions that you will have to make regarding your battery selection. You'll also have to consider other parameters, including battery voltage, capacity and power rating.

Voltage

The voltage usually depends on the load that you are powering. For small solar projects, like USB chargers that require 5 VDC, a low voltage battery is commonly used. Lead acid batteries generally come in 6 V increments which is helpful in this case, while li-ion batteries usually come in 3.6 V increments, which is less helpful and often requires the addition of a DC-DC converter to increase or decrease the voltage to the proper level for the project.

For home-based systems, the voltage of your battery is often affected by the voltage of your solar panel array. Most beginner solar panel arrays are 12 V. This is good for smaller setups and when the distance between the solar panels and the charge controller is fairly short, usually less than 50 ft (15 m). Longer distances will result in more resistance, which in turns results in a loss of power along the wire. This can be mitigated either by using thicker wires (which can get expensive over long wire runs) or by increasing the system voltage. Increasing the voltage allows you to use the same current but achieve higher power, or keep the power the same and decrease the current, since power in watts = volts x amps.

Depending on your charge controller though, you could be fairly limited in choosing your system voltage. PWM charge controllers work best with 12 VDC systems. Some can accept higher voltage up to 50 VDC, but that extra voltage will just be wasted if they are used to charge 12 V batteries. MPPT charge controllers can receive much higher voltages as they are true DC-DC converters, converting excess voltage into higher current at lower voltages. In this case, you can connect many solar panels in series to create high voltage DC that doesn't require exceedingly thick wires to reach the charge controller, and then the charge controller can convert that voltage down to something more realistic for your batteries, usually between 12-48 VDC.

While 12 VDC systems were more popular in the past due to all of the 12 VDC devices already available, 24 VDC and 48 VDC systems are quickly replacing many 12 VDC systems. Using higher voltage is simply more efficient and can actually save money on many components.

That isn't to say that 12 VDC isn't useful, but it is more applicable for smaller jobs, like tiny homes, RVs, cabins and boat houses. All of these applications have relatively short wire runs and lower power requirements. A 12 VDC system is useful up until the power requirements exceed approximately 2,000 to 2,500 watts. At that point, you're talking about current levels of over 200 A. Past this point, wiring, fuses and other components get very expensive, very quickly.

Higher voltage systems such as 24 VDC and 48 VDC systems solve this issue. Medium sized homes can get away with 24 VDC, which can provide reasonable current levels at power requirements of up to 4,000-5,000 W. Above those power levels, you really need to consider moving to a 48 VDC system. Using a 48 VDC system at power levels lower than 4,000 W is also fine, and will give you the added benefits of higher efficiency and many of the components being less expensive.

Don't think of 48 VDC as a hard limit. It's a common upper end for most home installations because it fits the power level that most homes require, but higher power demands might require higher voltage batteries of 60 VDC or even more. It all depends on how much power you need.

After you've decided on a voltage, you'll need to decide on whether you're going to build a battery bank yourself or buy one that is ready made. There are a number of lithium-ion battery packs that come ready for installation. The Tesla Powerwall is likely the most famous, but many other companies have their own versions as well. These don't require you to make any inter-battery connections yourself, as they arrive as one complete battery system.

On the other hand, most lead acid batteries come in lower voltage cells or packs of cells, usually either 2 V, 6 V or 12 V. These can be connected in series to create a battery of sufficient voltage. For example, earlier in this chapter I showed an example of deciding between an LG Chem lithium-ion battery bank and a Crown flooded lead acid battery bank. Because the flooded lead acid cells are only 2 V each and you purchase them individually, I had to buy 24 cells in that example, then connect them in series to create a 48 V battery.

Of course there are also companies that will do this work for you, or sell you a pre-built, self contained lead acid battery of the voltage you need. This option will cost more, but may be worth it for those seeking simplicity in their setup installation.

Lastly, you can build your own lithium batteries as well. This is a bit more complicated though, so I'll cover this in more detail in its own section at the end of this chapter.

Capacity

The capacity of a battery is usually measured in watt hours (Wh), which is a measure of how much energy can be stored in that battery. A watt hour literally means one watt of power supplied for one hour. For example, a 100 Wh battery can provide 100 watts for one hour before running out of charge. It could also provide 1 watt for 100 hours. Or 50 watts for 2 hours. Or 25 watts for 4 hours. Get it? Determining the runtime of a battery is as simple as dividing the watt hours by the load it will supply in watts.

Runtime = battery capacity in watt hours ÷ load in amps

This also works backwards. If you know that you have a 20 watt load, such as a light bulb, and you want it to run continuously for 10 hours, then you'll need to multiply the two together to get 200 watt hours. Powering that 20 watt light bulb for 10 hours requires 200 Wh of energy, or a 200 Wh battery pack.

Sometimes you'll see capacities listed in amp hours (Ah). Amp hours are a similar measurement, but they aren't as easily comparable between different voltage batteries. An amp hour works the same way, in that it means the battery can supply that many amps for an hour. Watt hours are better for comparisons between different voltage batteries though, so to convert Ah to Wh, simply multiply the Ah of the battery by the voltage of the battery. A 12 V battery rated for 10 Ah is a 120 Wh battery.

Watt hours of a battery = battery voltage x battery capacity in amp hours

Thus, if you compare two 10 Ah batteries, where one is a 12 V battery and the other is a 24 V battery, you can say that they have the same Ah rating, meaning they can both provide 10 A for an hour, but the 24 V battery actually has twice as much stored energy. That's because it has 240 Wh of energy, versus the 120 Wh of energy in the 12 V battery. Even though they can both provide 10 A of current for 1 hour, the 24 V battery will be providing twice as much power during that hour, since power in watts = volts x amps.

To determine the capacity of the battery that your project requires, it is usually easiest to think in watts, unless you already know the voltage and amperage of your loads. If I was making a solar powered flood light circuit for my backyard, and I knew that the lights in total draw a continuous 50 watts, and I knew that I wanted them to run for 10 hours at night, then I would need 500 Wh of energy to run those lights. That means I need at least a 500 Wh battery. If I want to use a 12 V system, then I can calculate how many amp hours I need by dividing 500 Wh by 12 V, to give me approximately 42 Ah. So I need to buy or build a 12 V battery rated for at least 42 Ah.

To plan an entire off-grid home, I'd use a similar system, except that I'd have to add up the wattage of everything I want to power in the house, from the fridge to the computer chargers to my wife's hair straightener. Then I'd need to determine how many hours each device would be used daily. Multiplying the wattage of each device by the hours per day it is in use will give me the daily watt-hours required by the device. Adding up all of the daily watt-hour requirements from around my house will give me a total energy requirement. A medium sized home might be 20-30 kWh, or 20,000 to 30,000 watt-hours. That's a big battery. It's also another reason that becoming more energy efficient at home is a big part of installing a solar power system, because it reduces your total energy consumption and thus the size (and cost) of your solar power system.

Power rating

Just as important as knowing how much energy you need over the runtime of your project or home, is knowing how much power you need. Draining 100 Wh of energy from a battery in a minute requires a lot more power than draining the same 100 Wh over the course of an hour, even though they both used the same total amount of energy. Using more energy at once indicates higher power.

Power, as we've already seen, is measured in watts. For larger numbers, it is easier to discuss power in units of kilowatts, which is 1,000 watts. In addition to knowing the total amount of energy your project uses, whether it is one charger for an electric boat or all of the appliances in your home, you also need to know the maximum instantaneous power that you'll need to draw.

For a single charger on an electric boat, that might just be 200 watts, which is the power rating of the charger. But for an entire home, you might want to be able to run a 1,500 watt microwave at the same time as a 1,000 watt hair dryer and a 200 watt television. That's a total of 2,700 watts of power that would need to be delivered at once. If your batteries aren't rated for 2,700 watts of continuous power, then you could be in trouble in the form of damaged batteries or a blackout when the battery's protection circuit kicks in to cut power in an overload scenario.

Larger lithium-ion batteries meant for home energy storage usually have their maximum power ratings listed in watts, but many smaller batteries might have it listed as a C rate. The C rate simply means the current that the battery can provide in proportion to its amp hour capacity. For example, a 48 V 10 Ah battery with a maximum discharge power of 1C can discharge at 10 amps. To determine this, you just multiply the Ah by the C rate. If the battery has a C rate of 2C, it can discharge at 20 amps, and if it has a C rate of 10C then it can discharge at an impressive 100 amps. To convert this C rate into watts, you can multiply the maximum amps by the voltage. So that 48 V 10 Ah battery with a 10C maximum discharge rate would have a discharge power of 4,800 W.

DIY lithium batteries

As explained in the sections above, most of the large lithium-ion battery banks that are designed for solar energy storage will already come pre-assembled by the manufacturer. The well known Tesla Powerwall is a great example of these types of batteries, but there are many companies out there building similar types of plug-and-play lithium-ion battery storage solutions.

These retail lithium-ion battery banks are great if you have the money, but with a bit of ingenuity, some handyman skills, and a lot of time and hard work, you can actually build your own large lithium-ion battery storage setups all by yourself. There are a few ways to do this, and we'll cover the basics here.

Whether you need a small battery for a pocket or backpack sized solar charger, a medium battery to power an electric boat or cabin, or a large battery to power an entire house, you can use the principles that I'll cover in this chapter to build an appropriately sized battery.

<u>Choosing the proper lithium-ion cells</u>

There are three main form factors of lithium-ion cells available for battery builders.

The first are called *pouch cells*. These look like an aluminum foil bag with two tabs sticking out of them. The tabs are the positive and negative terminals. They can be joined in series and parallel just like the terminals on any other battery cell. Some people solder the tabs together, though they can sometimes be difficult to solder. Others will drill a hole through the tabs (not through the pouch!) and bolt the tabs together. Still others will create bolting clamps that force the tabs together tightly. These are equally useful ways to achieve the same effect of electrically connecting the tabs to build larger packs.

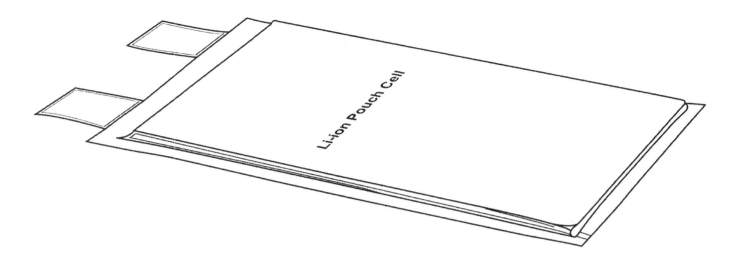

Pouch cells are fairly delicate, as the only thing protecting the inner layers of the lithium-ion cell is the thin foil pouch. When you work with bare pouch cells, you need to be extremely careful of two things: 1) not to accidentally puncture the pouch or cause any physical damage such as bending or dropping, and 2) not to let the two tab terminals short to each other by touching either each other (less common) or by the two tabs touching a metal object like a screwdriver, pair of pliers or any other common metal object (surprisingly common). Shorting a lithium cell doesn't just damage it, it can also be dangerous. Shorting a cell causes the cell to heat up due to the massive current flow in the short circuit. This can lead to a lithium-ion cell fire if the short circuit is allowed to continue for more than a few seconds.

Another common lithium-ion cell shape is the *prismatic cell*. These are often made of pouch cells that are contained within some type of rigid box, usually hard plastic. Prismatic cells have the advantage of being safer to use because the delicate cell inside is protected from accidental punctures or other damage. You still shouldn't drop them out of a window, but a drop of one or two feet usually isn't as damaging to a prismatic cell as it is to a pouch cell. The hard case on a prismatic cell also means you don't need to do as much work to build a suitable holder for bare cells, like you would for pouch cells.

Another advantage of prismatic cells is that they usually have nice big terminals on top of the cell that are easy to connect. Unlike pouch cells, which have bare tab terminals that require custom connection solutions like soldering or clamping, prismatic cells usually have bolt or lug terminals. This can save a lot of time during battery building.

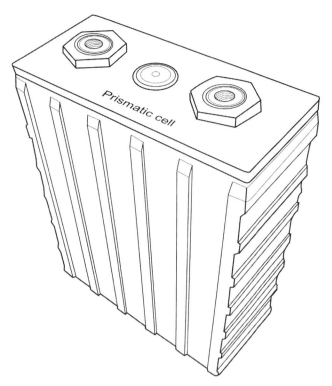

The last major advantage of prismatic cells is that they are often available in much larger capacities than other types of li-ion cells. This means fewer parallel connections, which means fewer things to worry about during the construction phase of your battery. However, larger capacity cells can also be a disadvantage. If for some reason a cell dies, having fewer cells in parallel means having to replace more of your battery. If you had four small cells in a parallel group and one died, you only have to replace a quarter of that parallel group. But if you just had one big cell in that group and it died, you'll be forking over the cash for another big cell.

While li-ion and LiFePO$_4$ chemistries are available in all form factors, LiFePO$_4$ is mostly available in prismatic cells. So if you plan to use LiFePO$_4$ (which we talked about earlier in this chapter), then prismatic cells might be a good option for you.

The third and last form factor available for lithium-ion battery builders is the *cylindrical cell*, which happens to be my favorite. A cylindrical cell is just a pouch cell that has been rolled up and stuffed into a cylindrical can. Most of the alkaline batteries you use regularly, like the AAs in a flashlight or TV remote control, are examples of cylindrical cells. Most lithium-ion cylindrical cells are a bit bigger than common alkaline cells though.

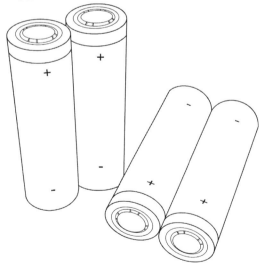

The most common cylindrical cell is the 18650, named after its size of 18 mm in diameter and 65 mm in length. However, slightly larger 20700 and 21700 (also written as 2070 and 2170) cells are also gaining in popularity. 18650 cells have been commonly used since the early 2000s, while the larger 20700 and 21700 cells only became popular in the mid-to-late 2010s. This means that there is still much more variety available in 18650 cells, though that will likely change in the coming decade.

Most 18650 sized cells are li-ion, and you usually don't find LiFePO$_4$ cylindrical cells until you get to sizes of 26650 or larger. Larger LiFePO$_4$ cells in the 38120, 38140 and 40152 sizes are also popular. These sizes often come with threaded terminals on each end, which makes it easier to join them, unlike most 18650 and 26650 sized cells, which usually have bare terminals that require other forms of connections.

Among the three form factors of cells available, all are possible options for custom battery builders. If you're building a small pack, such as one that can fit in your hands, prismatic cells will probably be too large for your needs. At that point, either pouch cells or small cylindrical cells such as 18650s are a better option. For larger battery packs, including those for vehicles or homes, all three options are possible. Prismatic cells will be the easiest to join into large packs, pouch cells will likely be the most energy dense, and cylindrical cells will give you the most customizability and options due the extremely wide availability of cylindrical cells compared to prismatic and pouch cells.

Acquiring lithium-ion battery cells

Lithium-ion battery cells are available from a large number of different online retailers, though shipping can often be quite expensive due to their designation as hazardous materials. Hazmat certification is often required to transport lithium batteries over a certain size or quantity.

If you want to make your purchase online, then purchasing lithium-ion battery cells from a reputable solar energy website is the best method. They will be well schooled in the methods and laws of shipping lithium-ion batteries.

You might also have a local solar energy parts dealer that you can purchase from directly. This might help you save on shipping, but in many cases the dealer will still be required to have the batteries delivered to you for legal reasons. Plus, buying locally limits your options to shop around and price compare. However, the added benefit of having a local dealer for warranty and service can help you sleep better at night, especially considering the cost of some of these larger lithium battery systems.

If you want the cheapest prices on lithium-ion cells though, you've got to go to China. Well, not really *go* to China, but you know what I mean. Websites like Alibaba and AliExpress, among others, connect buyers around the world to Chinese sellers, and use Escrow systems to ensure fair transactions. Alibaba is great for buying large numbers of parts at wholesale prices, while AliExpress is better for smaller quantities while still getting near wholesale pricing.

The main problem with buying directly from China is ensuring that you're working with a good seller that has genuine products. Fake lithium-ion cells are all over the place in China. In fact, there might be more fakes than real ones at this point. While fake cells usually work, they aren't made to the same quality control standards as the genuine cells made by reputable manufacturers and are usually lower capacity than indicated.

Making matters worse, it can often be difficult to tell the difference between fake and genuine lithium-ion cells without performing discharge testing of each cell and comparing to the manufacturer's specifications. If purchasing from China, it is best to visit online forums related to solar energy or battery building and learn from others in the same situation as you. People share which vendors can be trusted and which have sent them poor quality products. As vendors change, recommendations also change, so it is recommended to stay up to date on this information.

Buying lithium-ion battery cells from China can save you a lot of money by cutting out the middleman, but it does increase your risk of getting fake products. This is something you have to weigh carefully.

Regardless of where you buy your cells from, new lithium-ion battery cells are expensive. For many people, they are prohibitively expensive.

But we humans are a resourceful species, and some very clever people have found ways to salvage lithium-ion battery cells from old electronics and use them for custom batteries built for solar energy storage. This community is known by the term DIY Powerwall, as in people who make their own versions of the well known Tesla Powerwall. Obviously these won't be of the same quality as Tesla's products, but the idea is to produce something that works almost as well for a small fraction of the cost.

The name of this game is to scavenge battery packs from discarded consumer goods. The most common source is laptop batteries. The batteries used for DIY powerwalls are almost always cylindrical cells, and usually 18650 cylindrical cells. Many laptops use between three to nine 18650 batteries in their removable battery packs. As these batteries can have useful lifespans of many years, they often outlast the computer itself, which quickly becomes obsolete. Thus, people throw out the entire laptop, even though the battery pack might still have most of its useful life remaining. It's a pity, but that's our world.

And it's not just limited to laptop batteries. Robotic vacuum cleaners, medical equipment, radios, power tools, and many other devices that use cylindrical battery packs will end up being discarded long before their batteries are even close to dying. All of these batteries are a goldmine for scrupulous battery builders that can salvage them on the cheap.

It used to be incredibly easy to find these discarded battery packs. On eBay you could buy big lots of them for a few bucks. Many computer repair stores were giving them away just to avoid having to deal with sending them to a recycling center. Recycling centers were often selling them by the pound for the same reason - it was easier to hand them off to eager battery builders than to go through the recycling process. Supply was high and demand was comparatively low.

Now though, demand has increased. Supply is still high, as there are always people throwing out perfectly good things, but it has become somewhat harder to find these discarded battery packs due to the increased demand. Where they are available, the prices have increased, turning discarded battery packs from a waste product to something of a commodity. Searching around for local computer repair shops, scrap collectors and recycling centers can still be a good way to find these hidden treasures.

Once you find your battery packs, you'll have to harvest the cylindrical cells inside. This can be one of the most time consuming steps, comparable to shelling oysters. Most battery packs aren't designed to be opened easily, so many have to be cut or cracked open. It is best to do this carefully to avoid damaging the cells inside, but fortunately 18650 cells are fairly robust due to their steel cans. Thus, many people just smack the battery packs on the floor until they crack open. It is not recommended, but it works for many people.

Once you get the batteries out, you'll have to pull them apart. They are usually spot welded together with strips of nickel, so you need to use pliers to pull off the nickel. This will often leave little bits of nickel stuck to the cell terminals, which can usually be removed with a Dremmel-style rotary tool or grinding wheel. Again, be careful not to damage your cells.

Next, you need to test your batteries. Remember, these things came out of the trash, so not all of them are going to be good. The best way to test is to start by using a voltmeter. You want to find cells that are above 2.5 V. Cells that are lower can sometimes be saved, but they will die much quicker than healthier cells, so you might not want to put them in your pack and have them dragging down other cells with them. Cells that are at 0 V are simply goners. Anything above 4.2 V per cell is dangerous, and you don't want to mess with those cells. However, that would be a very rare find, indicating something went wrong the last time that cell was charged. You'll also want to remove any cells that look physically damaged or have exterior corrosion on them.

Once you've found the cells with proper voltage ranges, you need charge them all up to 4.2 V (the full voltage charge of li-ion cells) and let them sit for a minimum of three to four days, but a week or more is better. If any cells then show a voltage drop of more than 0.1-0.2 V, that's an indication that the cell is bad. It won't hold its charge, so it shouldn't go into your battery pack. You can also note some bad cells by measuring their temperature with a laser or infrared thermometer. Cells that get exceedingly hot should be watched and potentially removed from the group of good cells. If you are only building a small pack and you don't want to invest in a cheap infrared thermometer, you can just touch the batteries to feel their temperature. If it is scalding hot during charging or discharging, its a bad cell.

Next you need to individually test each cell's capacity. This is a time consuming step, depending on how many cells you test, but it is essential to make sure your cells aren't old and worn out. There are a number of four-cell 18650 capacity testers out there, most available in the $30-50 range. They have four bays for single 18650s and measure the capacity of each cell. Better ones also measure the internal resistance. If you're only testing a few dozen cells, then a single four-cell tester is probably fine. If you have hundreds or thousands of cells, you'll probably want to invest in a few testers. Otherwise you could spend months or even years testing your battery cells four at a time.

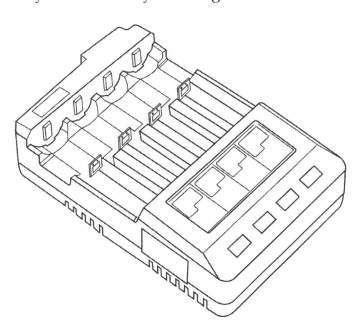

Opus-style 18650 battery tester

Testing each battery cell will determine its capacity. You want to weed out any cells that have low capacities. "Low" varies depending on who you talk to, but many people draw the line at about 1,900-2,000 mAh. Others are happy to use cells with lower capacities, understanding that these cells aren't likely to be as powerful or last as long. Many new cells used in laptops start at around 2,200-2,500 mAh, so very low capacities indicate the cell is likely quite old and worn out. Such cells still have some capacity left, as indicated by your tester, but that capacity isn't very usable because they will drain very fast under heavier loads and their already minimal capacity will only decrease over time. Such cells are near the end of their lives and could drag down good cells around them if included in a larger pack. Once you've determined the capacity of the cell, write it on the wrapper of the cell with a permanent marker. This will help you classify them later when you begin building your battery.

Some cell testers also measure the internal resistance of cells, though these cheap testers are not very accurate for internal resistance measurements. This measurement is usually only helpful for finding cells with extremely high resistances. A brand new 18650 usually has an internal resistance of between 30-50 milliohms. As they get older, their internal resistance will increase. Some people will toss cells with internal resistance measurements above 150 milliohms, while others will start weeding cells out at 200 or 250 milliohms. The exact figure isn't as important as knowing that higher internal resistance is another indication of being closer to the end of the cell's useful life cycle. It is fine if your tester doesn't measure internal resistance, as capacity measurements are usually enough to weed out the bad cells.

You should expect to toss more than half of your cells during this culling stage. If you can find that 40% of your cells are above 2,000 mAh, consider that a good haul. Over 50% of cells being usable would be great, but it is rare. Any reject cells should be sent to your local recycler. There are still salvageable materials in there and they shouldn't just sit in a landfill. Plus, it is illegal in many areas to throw lithium-ion batteries in with municipal garbage waste.

Once you've separated your good cells, you'll want to group them according to the battery size that you need. It is best to keep cells with similar mAh ratings together in the same parallel groups if you're using a bleeding Battery Management System (BMS), as it will make the balancing much quicker and easier.

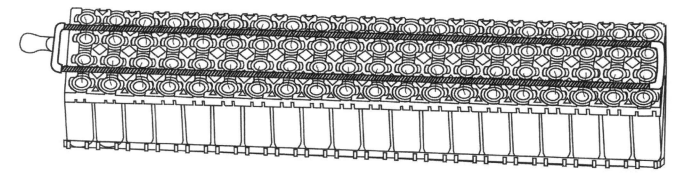

DIY powerwall-style 18650 battery module

To construct parallel groups, the generally accepted method is to use black 18650 grid cell holders. These are cheaply available on sites like Ebay, Amazon and AliExpress. Simply pop your cells into the holes in the grid and then put a second holder on the other side, sandwiching the cells together into a big module. All of the cells should be facing the same direction, with positive terminals on one side and negative terminals on the other side. Large powerwalls often use 80p modules, or 80 cells in parallel in a 4x20 configuration, but your needs will determine how many cells you use. For example, if your cells average 2,000 mAh, and you need 120 Ah per parallel module, then you could use 60 cells in each parallel module.

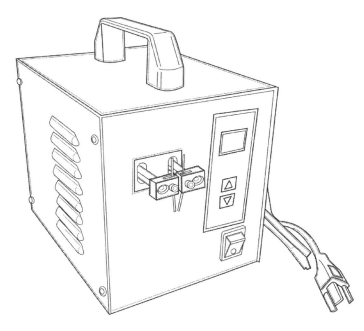

A common budget-level spot welder

At this point, most DIY powerwall builders solder their cells together. Consider this a safety disclaimer: 18650 cells are not intended to be soldered. Manufacturers will tell you not to do it and that their cells aren't meant for it. It adds a lot of heat to the cell and can damage the cell. However, most DIY powerwall builders still solder their cells simply because it is cheap. If you go this route, you're on your own, as it is not recommended by cell manufacturers. Spot welding is the manufacturer-recommended method for joining cells together. However, most people don't own or want to invest in a spot welder. Cheap ones start at around $150, and expensive ones can cost many thousands of dollars.

If you do choose to solder your cells, despite this not being recommended, this is how it is done. A thick gauge copper wire is bent into a bus bar so that it runs next to all cells in a module. Then, a thin fuse wire is soldered to the 18650 cell terminal on one side and the copper bus bar on the other. This fuse is there as a safety mechanism. If the cell ever experiences a short circuit, the fuses will blow, disconnecting the cell from the pack and preventing it from dragging other cells down and destroying the entire module.

Once you have completed a parallel module like this, you'll create as many more as necessary for combining in series to achieve the voltage of your system. This is generally 12, 24 or 48 V for a home solar energy storage bank, but could theoretically be any voltage depending on your project. For a 12 V system, three or four modules are used in series. For a 24 V system, seven modules are usually used in series, and for a 48 V system, 14 modules are usually used in series. You can achieve other custom voltages by changing the number of batteries in series, using 3.6 V or 3.7 V as the nominal voltage of the pack, and multiplying that number by the number of series groups to determine the larger pack's nominal voltage.

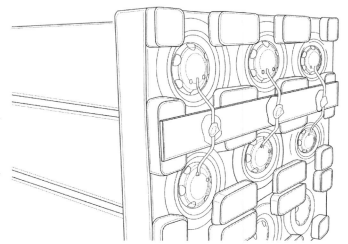

Fuse wires soldered to copper bus bar

Note: If you'd like to build a powerwall like this, I highly recommend spending time on the forum DIYpowerwall.com and learning from the many experienced and knowledgeable members.

While this is the most common way to build a DIY powerwall (using black plastic cell spacer grids and soldering) there are other options available too. Multiple kits have now entered the market that allow the user to join 18650 cells together without soldering them. They usually use conductive plates that are clamped onto the 18650 cell terminals by bolts, or snap together caps that achieve the same effect. They all offer the opportunity to remove 18650 cells and replace them if they ever go bad, and don't require any soldering or spot welding. I am associated with a company that offers one of these kits, but because this is an informational book, I don't want to mix marketing into it, so I won't specifically list my kit or any others. But you can google around and compare different solderless battery building kit options to see if one works well for you.

Cylindrical cells such as 18650s aren't the only option for building custom batteries, they are just one of the cheapest and most customizable. However, an easier method is to use larger prismatic lithium-ion batteries. These come in a wide range of sizes, but are often around the size of car batteries. They also have convenient terminals on them, just like car batteries, that allow them to be connected easily - no soldering or spot welding required! You may have to get a good crimping tool though so you can make strong wire connectors to join these cells. Alternatively, many come as kits with bus bars that allow you to join the prismatic cells without any wiring.

Just like in the DIY powerwall with 18650 cells, you'll need to join enough prismatic cells in series and parallel to achieve the proper voltage and capacity for your system. The nice thing about prismatic cells it that you'll have many fewer cells to join. While most 18650s range from 2 to 3.5 Ah, prismatic cells often start at 10 Ah and can be as large as hundreds of amp-hours.

Regardless of the method you use to join your lithium battery cells together, you'll need some type of Battery Management System (BMS) to monitor the charging and discharging process. For DIY powerwalls, many people use a system made by Batrium that protects your battery cells and allows you to monitor their health in real time on a computer. For smaller projects though, a simple bleeding BMS is often sufficient. These BMSs function by monitoring the parallel groups in the battery during charging, and then slightly drain the cells that reach full voltage first to allow the lower voltage cells to catch up. This effectively balances the battery, but takes longer on larger batteries.

Note: The process of building a lithium battery can be complicated and dangerous if you don't know what you are doing. This chapter was designed to present the process to you, but not make you an expert. If you want to learn about battery building in detail, including the theory, design, construction steps and more, I highly recommend my book DIY Lithium Batteries: How To Build Your Own Battery Packs. It solely focuses on battery construction and contains much more information, detail and step-by-step instructions than I could fit in a chapter in this book.

Chapter 5: Sourcing solar panels

Solar panels are the most important part of your solar setup. Without them, it doesn't matter how much sun is shining - you're not going to be able to convert it into the electricity you need! However, before you can buy your solar panels, you'll need to know which ones to choose. There are a few different types available, and we'll cover them here.

PV cells, the individual units that are joined to create solar panels, mainly come in two varieties: *monocrystalline* and *polycrystalline* PV cells. Monocrystalline PV cells are made from high purity silicone that comes in a cylindrical ingot. They are cut down on the sides and then sliced to create wafers, resulting in the distinctive rounded edge PV cells.

Polycrystalline PV cells are made from somewhat less pure raw molten silicon that is heated and poured into a mold, resulting in the perfectly rectangular edges. You can tell them apart from monocrystalline PV cells because the polycrystalline PV cells have four 90-degree corners and a non-uniform, speckled appearance.

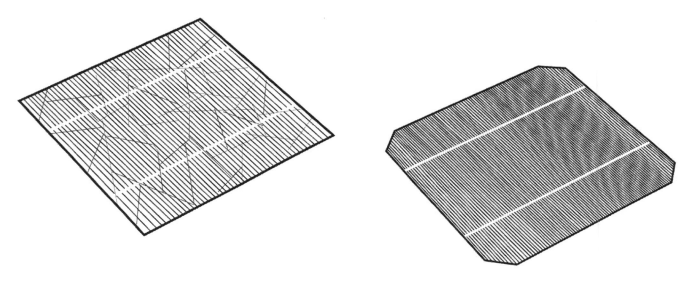

Left: Polycrystalline PV cell; Right: Monocrystalline PV cell

Due to their higher silicon purity, monocrystalline PV cells are somewhat more efficient than polycrystalline PV cells at converting sunlight into electricity, though this difference is not usually a large factor for most solar installations, as the added cost balances out the added efficiency. That means you can just buy more polycrystalline PV cells to create the same amount energy for the same total cost. A more important factor for many people is that monocrystalline PV cells are more space efficient, which if you have limited space for solar panels, can make a big difference.

Other advantages of monocrystalline PV cells are that they generally last longer, resulting in longer manufacturer's warranties, and they also work better in high heat and low light than polycrystalline PV cells.

While monocrystalline PV cells have several advantages over polycrystalline cells, some of the factors aren't very significant for most people. Plus, there's one area where polycrystalline cells have a major advantage - price. They are consistently cheaper than monocrystalline cells, which can be a deciding factor in many installations. If you don't need the highest efficiency per square foot or square meter and can accept the somewhat shorter lifespan, you can save money by choosing solar panels made from polycrystalline cells.

These aren't the only types of PV cells available, but they are the most useful for standard solar projects. A third category known as "thin film" solar panels is also available. These panels have the advantage of being much more flexible and can even be rolled into tubes, however they have around half the efficiency of mono- and polycrystalline solar panels. Unless you absolutely need a highly flexible solar panel, thin film solar cells aren't likely to be a good choice for cost and efficiency reasons.

Other types of PV cells include amorphous silicon PV cells, which have even lower efficiency rates than thin film solar cells and are mostly used for extremely low power devices, Cadmium Telluride PV cells, which also suffer from low efficiencies but have made recent improvements, and Copper Indium Gallium Selenide PV cells, which are also in a similar situation to Cadmium Telluride PV cells. However, all of these are still rare compared to mono and polycrystalline PV cells. It is uncommon to find them outside of a few specialty applications.

Once you've decided which type of solar panel is right for your project, you'll have a couple of options for purchasing them. You can either buy the panels ready-to-install, or you can buy bare PV cells and build your own solar panels. Ready-to-install panels are usually better for large solar installations, unless you really want to penny pinch and have the time to solder together thousands of PV cells. If you're just building a small solar setup though, it might be worth it to consider building your own solar panel(s) out of individual PV cells.

Purchasing pre-made solar panels

There's a lot of DIYing to be done in a solar setup, so I don't blame you if you don't want the extra work of soldering together a massive pile of solar cells. Plus, for most people installing a large solar array for their home, the peace of mind that comes with a professional installer and a long warranty can be quite comforting.

When you're ready to begin shopping around for your solar panels, you'll of course want to compare prices. The standard metric for comparison in the solar world is $/watt. Currently, large residential solar panels in the 200 W range can usually be purchased for around $200-$300 per panel, or somewhat less when buying 10 or 20 panels for an entire home setup. This works out to around $1 to $1.50/W for a single panel, or closer to $0.75/W for many panels, which is quite good. A few years ago these panels cost two to three times as much, so consider yourself lucky!

Obviously prices will vary from different vendors and for different panels. As a rule of thumb, larger panels usually have lower $/W and smaller panels have higher $/W. A 10 W panel might still cost you $20-$50, depending where you buy it.

There are a number of websites online that sell and ship solar panels. This can be a good place to do research and investigate different sizes of panels, manufacturers and price ranges. If you are fortunate enough to have a local solar panel installer in your area though, I recommend talking with them at some point. Not only will they be experts on solar panel installation in case you need any help, but they might be able to give you better prices by saving on shipping costs. Large solar panels are not cheap to ship.

As solar-powered homes become more common, increasing competition between new solar providers is helping consumers by driving down prices. However, you may not always want to go with the cheapest option. Make sure you look for a company that has been around for a while and has good reviews. A 25-year warranty doesn't mean much if the company goes bankrupt next year.

Building DIY solar panels

There is an alternative to buying pre-made solar panels. If you don't mind the extra labor, building your own can be a great solution. As mentioned, you're foregoing a warranty this way, so keep that in mind.

Individual solar cells can be purchased quite inexpensively. Currently, a kit to build a 100 W solar panel costs just $50 from China, bringing the price down to $0.50/W. By buying higher numbers of PV cells at once, you can reduce the $/W even further. A set of 100 pieces of 5 W monocrystalline cells costs $150, working out to $0.30/W, not including some extra parts that must be added to build the finished panels, such as the frame and glass.

These cheap PV solar cells make a bigger difference if you're building smaller solar panels than if you're building large solar panel arrays. As you buy larger solar panels and in larger quantities, the price becomes more reasonable, even dropping below $1/W. However, the price per watt is still quite high on small solar panels, especially for panels below 50 watts. Smaller solar panels meant for charging devices and carrying on-the-go can still cost as much as $5/W, or five times the price of larger panels. For these smaller panels, building your own can help save significant resources.

The reason that larger DIY solar panels often aren't much cheaper than retail solar panels usually comes down to the frame. Even though the solar cells are cheaper per watt, you still have to enclose them somehow to protect them. Glass or epoxy usually covers the front of the solar cells, while a rigid frame of wood or aluminum holds the structure and keeps it rigid. These costs increase as you scale up, often making the cost savings versus large pre-made solar panels negligible, especially considering the extra labor involved. For small projects, on the other hand, a little bit of wood and small piece of glass aren't very expensive and can often be salvaged for free from other projects or items, like an old picture frame.

Building a DIY solar panel from PV cells

Building a DIY solar panel starts with determining how many PV cells you'll need. This is determined by the voltage and current requirements of your project. Common voltages include 5 V systems for USB charging, and standard 12 V and 24 V systems for battery charging. A typical 5 V system will use 12 cells in series to make 6 V, while 12 V and 24 V systems use 36 and 72 cells in series to create 18 and 36 V systems, respectively. As we discussed previously, the open circuit voltage of the solar panels is higher than the required voltage because the voltage will sag when a load is applied, and the charge controller will further reduce the voltage to the appropriate level for the battery.

Next, you'll need to decide whether you want to start with bare PV cells or pre-tabbed PV cells. The main difference is the amount of work you'll need to perform. Bare PV cells are cheaper, but you'll need to go through the time consuming task of soldering tabbing wire, usually included in kits with the PV cells, onto the fronts of all of the cells. Tabbed cells already have the tabs included on the cells.

One other option is to purchased broken PV cells. You can usually get these for much cheaper than Grade A bare PV cells. These are cells that have been broken or chipped in the production process. Chipped solar panels will have a somewhat reduced power output, but are usually still functional as long as the chip is fairly small. They can't be sold with new, unblemished cells, but are still desirable to DIY solar panel builders. If you want the cheapest PV cells and don't mind somewhat lower output power, chipped PV cells can be a good option. Just make sure you try to use PV cells that all have a similar amount of missing cell area, as the smallest PV cell will be the limiting factor in the entire series string. Also, check each cell with a voltmeter to ensure that it is in fact producing voltage under sunlight before using it in a solar panel.

Whether you use new or chipped PV cells, you'll need to add tabbing wire if the cells didn't come with it. To apply the tab wire, cut a length that is twice the height the of the solar cell. Use a flux pen, usually available in kits for DIY solar panels, and apply a line of flux along the front of the PV cell (the dark side with the little lines on it, which is the negative terminal of the PV cell). Using a soldering iron, solder the tab wire to the front of the solar cell, allowing the second half of the tab wire to hang off the top or bottom edge of the cell. Either direction is fine, as turning the cell upside down produces the same effect. It can often be helpful to use another tool to help hold the tabbing wire down while you solder it.

Once all of your cells are tabbed, you'll need to join as many in series as necessary to obtain your proper voltage. If you need a voltage higher than 12 V (which would require 36 cells in series to reach approximately 18-20 V open circuit) then you might want to stick with 36 cells per panel and simply create two panels that you'll wire in series. This will reduce the size and complexity of your panels.

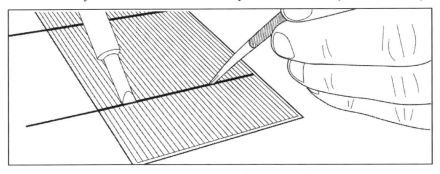

Using tweezers to help solder PV cell tabs

Lay all of your cells positive side up, meaning that the negative front that is already tabbed will be down on your work surface. It is helpful to lay all of the cells on a large sheet of cardboard or panel of wood so you can move the arrangement around if necessary.

Next, drape the tabs from the first PV cell over the terminals of the second cell. Continue following this pattern to create a long series chain of cells. Depending on the size of your panel, you'll need to create an S pattern with switchbacks when you reach the end of the panel so you can continue your series chain. To do this you will need to use bus wire, which is essentially just thicker tabbing wire. Lay your bus wire as shown in the diagram, so that the tabs from the positive back of the last cell in the column rest on the bus bar, then the tabs from the negative front side of the first solar cell in the next column also rest on the bus wire.

PV cell layout showing 36 cells connected in series

Continue with this pattern until you have laid all of your solar cells out in a series format. You might have to do multiple S bends to fit all of your solar cells in the required space.

Once you have all of your cells laid out, you can solder the tabbing wire from one cell to the next. Use a flux pen on the positive terminals on the back of the solar cell before soldering to help make a stronger solder joint.

After soldering on the tabbing wire, it can be helpful to use packing or strapping tape to hold the PV cells together. This allows you to move the entire string around without relying on the mechanical soldering connections. While the cells are still face down, lay packing or strapping tape across the backside of the cells, connecting them all together. Leave a little bit of tape extending in all directions to allow you to move and slide the string of solar cells around by pulling on the tape instead of pulling on the cells themselves.

Once you have all of your cells soldered and taped together, you'll need to add your wires and a blocking diode. A blocking diode only allows current to flow one-way through a circuit. This ensures that if your solar panel isn't in the sun, such as at night or when in the shade, your battery doesn't try to send current back through it the wrong way. Most charge controllers and inverters have blocking diodes in them, but it is still a good idea to include one in your solar panel just in case. It is important to get the directionality correct though. The striped part of the diode should be pointing out from the positive wire of the solar panel, which means the other side (without the strip) will be connected to the backside of your last solar cell.

Always make sure that your blocking diode is rated for sufficient current and voltage. For most solar panels, a 5 A and 60 V rated blocking diode will be enough, and should only cost a few dollars. If you have a high wattage panel that can provide more than 5 A though, you'll want to make sure you choose an appropriately rated diode.

Your wiring should also be sufficiently rated for your power needs. For most panels, 12 AWG wire is sufficient, but thinner wire is acceptable for smaller panels. Online wire calculators are helpful tools to determine what gauge wire you will need based on your specific voltage, current and wire length parameters.

Lastly, you'll need to put your solar cells in some type of frame. If you can find an old picture frame, this can be a great solution for medium to large size solar panels, since it already provides a rigid frame with glass. Just be sure to use silicone caulk to seal the panel edges and keep water out. Otherwise you'll end up with condensation on the inside of your glass.

You can also build your own frame using wood. I like to take a 2x4 and rip it in half on a table saw. Then, I set the saw blade for half of the thickness of the wood and cut it on two adjacent sides, removing a notch from the wood. This creates a shelf that a panel of glass can sit on. Use a miter saw to cut 45° corners on four pieces, or just connect them at right angles, creating a rectangular frame. Then cut a piece of plywood to also fit inside of the notch. Use enamel paint to seal the wood, then lay a bead of silicone caulk all the way around the inside of the notch. Next,

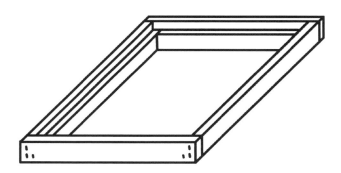

Simple notched wooden frame

place the glass, followed by the solar cells and finally the plywood into the notch, followed by another bead of caulk behind the plywood. Don't forget to drill a hole in the frame or plywood for the wires and also caulk around the wires to prevent water from entering the frame.

The third option is to encase the solar cells in an epoxy resin. This can be done by building a frame just like in the previous example. Drill a hole for the wires in the frame, then lay down a bead of silicone caulk in the notch, followed by placing the glass onto the silicone. Next, lay the PV cells down onto the glass. You'll want to use packing or strapping tape to tape the PV cells down to the glass and prevent epoxy from getting between the glass the cells. Finally, mix the two parts of epoxy in a mixing jar, measuring the appropriate amount for the volume you want to fill behind the PV cells, and pour into the frame on top of the backs of the solar cells. Make sure the epoxy also fills in the hole where the wires exit the frame. Allow it to cure overnight before moving the panel.

Be sure to research the epoxy you are using thoroughly. Ideally you want to use an epoxy that has high UV resistance. Some cheap epoxies can turn yellow or cloudy quickly when exposed to UV radiation.

At this point, you now know how to buy or build the solar panels you need for your project. Now it's time to build something! We'll start by looking at smaller projects first, covered in the next chapter, then we'll expand to larger projects for vehicles and homes.

Chapter 6: Small scale solar electricity

Solar power is amazing for powering big projects like homes and vehicles (which we'll cover in later chapters) but perhaps one of my favorite uses for solar power is for small scale projects. These could be anything from table top projects to camping/hiking chargers and even small solar installations such as well pumps or motion activated lights. Solar power is great for these types of projects because it allows you collect and use energy in the form of electricity in places far from an electrical outlet or a large backup battery. And because many of these projects are so small, they are easy to take with you out into the wild, or anywhere else you plan to go!

Load identification

The first step for small solar electricity projects, which is similar to most solar projects in general, is determining your energy demands. This will be important for all types of projects because it will help you choose the size of solar panels you'll need and also how much battery power and capacity you'll require, if you need batteries.

For single continuous loads, determining the energy demand is usually fairly easy. Let's consider string lights that you'd like to use for a multi-day camping trip. You could use a few strings of 12V LED rope lights, for example. One way to determine their energy draw is to check the box or label on the lights. Hopefully they are marked in a clear way, such as being labeled as 5 W per string. If you have four strings of lights, that's a total of 20 W of power. To determine their energy use though, you'd need to multiply their power, in watts, by the number of hours you plan to use them. Assuming you want the lights to run for five hours a night, that's a total of 100 watt hours. That means you'll need a solar setup that can provide at least 100 watt hours of energy per day into a battery that can hold at least 100 watt hours of energy.

Energy in watt hours = continuous power in watts x length of runtime in hours

This is the same process you'll use for any small solar project. Consider a case where you are building a solar powered water pump. If you have a 12 VDC pump that uses 150 W of power, and you know that you'll need at least 30 minutes of pumping per day, you'll multiply 150 W by 0.5 hours to get 75 watt hours. Notice that I converted minutes to hours here to ensure that my units remain in watt hours. Technically, "watt minutes" could be an acceptable unit as well, but then you'd have to perform all of your calculations in minutes, which could become frustrating because everything in this industry uses watt hours as the standard unit.

If you need to power multiple loads from the same solar panel and/or battery, you'll simply add up the total watt hours of each device per day. For example, if we also wanted to use our water pump while camping, perhaps to pump water up from a nearby stream to our camp site, we'd add up the total watt hours for the combined system. Adding 100 watt hours of energy for lights each day and 75 watt hours for pumping each day means that our entire daily energy use would be 175 watt hours for the combined system.

Of course if we already have that running stream nearby, maybe we should have rigged up a hydroelectric generator to power the pump and lights. But that's another topic for another day!

System usage requirements

Once you know the energy needs of your system, you must determine if you'll need the energy continuously all day and night, just occasionally on demand, or you'll only need the energy during the day when the sun is out.

Continuous 24-hour usage means you'll need to be generating enough energy from your solar panel(s) to both power your device and store power for the rest of the day. That usually means you'll need to plan on capturing enough energy in 6-8 hours to last for 24 hours, or up to 4x as much energy as you consume at any one instant. And that's just enough to last for a single day, assuming you never have a cloudy day. An example of a real-world scenario like this could be a warning beacon on a floating buoy. The beacon is on all the time, and needs a solar panel that can keep its battery charged to last through the night and cloudy days.

Occasional use means you might be able to get away with the opposite - a very small panel relative to your batteries. In this scenario, you'll be slowly saving up solar energy in your battery so that it's there for sporadic, heavier draws. After a heavy draw, you'd go back to slowly storing up power again to prepare for the next draw. An example of this could be the well pump we discussed earlier. You might only need to draw from the well a couple times per day or week, depending on how you use your well. If that's the case, you could have a smaller solar panel and a larger battery.

If you only need solar power during the day, you might be able to completely forgo a battery bank, since you won't need stored power (assuming you also don't need to run your devices on cloudy days). This means your system could be much simpler and require fewer parts. An example of this could be a dedicated solar power USB charger for a phone or tablet. There are solar powered USB chargers that include backup batteries, but the battery makes them larger and heavier than they need to be. When hiking you don't want to carry more weight than you need, so a solar-only charger would mean that you could charge your devices when the sun is out and not need the excess weight of batteries, inverters or charge controllers. Something like this would be easy to strap to the outside of your pack and charge all day without thinking about it. However, you'd better hope your phone battery lasts if you get stuck with a rainy day.

Solar component selection

The type and size of solar panel(s) you choose will largely be determined by the energy requirements you calculated above, both the total required energy use and the amount of on-demand energy use necessary.

Non-continuous use systems are much easier, because you can get away with relatively smaller solar panels, especially if the energy use is fairly sporadic. If we go back to our pump example, we can determine the solar panel requirements for that specific case. We already know the pump uses 150 watts of power at 12 VDC. That means that it pulls approximately 12.5 amps of current. But that doesn't mean that we need a solar panel that can provide 150 watts or 12.5 amps - we can use a much lower power panel since our battery will serve as a buffer! We calculated above that half an hour of use per day at 150 watts of power is 75 watt hours of energy. So all we need is a panel that can generate at least 75 watt hours of energy per day. If we can bank on 7.5 hours of good sun, that could be as little as 10 watt hours every hour, which means we'd need a 10 watt panel. That's much smaller than a 150 watt panel!

Of course that is assuming 7.5 hours of good sun and that the panel will give exactly 10 W. In reality, you should plan on your panel getting at most 75% of its rated power, and probably less than that. To be safe, let's plan on achieving two thirds of the solar panel's rated power, and let's also assume we'll only get 5 hours of sun per day, in case there are clouds or shade, etc. With just 5 hours of sun, we'd need 15 watts of power to generate 75 watt hours (15 watts x 5 hours = 75 watt hours). But that 15 watt panel is not really going to give us 15 watts - we're assuming it will realistically give us something closer to two thirds, which is only 10 watts. If we had a 25 W panel though, two thirds of that would be slightly more than 16 watts. Since we need 15 watts of power over 5 continuous hours, a 25 W panel will be great. At 16 watts of actual power, if we get more than 5 hours of sun or the panel performs at better than two thirds of its rated power, we'll even generate extra electricity that day.

We also need a battery that can store 75 watt hours of energy if we want to be able to run that pump for 30 minutes in a row. At 12 V, our 75 Wh battery is a 6.25 Ah battery. Any battery that can hold at least 6.25 Ah will allow us to run our 150 W 12 VDC pump for 30 minutes straight. In reality, we'll lose some energy due to inefficiencies in the wire and pump, but it should be close to 30 minutes. If we want to store any excess energy we generate that day, just in case we have a cloudy day or we want to pump extra that day, we'll need a 12 V battery that is larger than 6.25 Ah. The smallest lead acid batteries usually come in increments of 7, 10, and 12 Ah SLA bricks, meaning we have decent options for battery sizes. Lithium batteries, especially custom built ones from 18650 cells, can start at increments as low as 2 Ah, so there is even more room for customizability when building a battery that can hold the exact amount of energy you need.

This was an example where your solar panel can actually provide less power than your device needs. Here, our pump is rated at 150 watts but we only need a 25 watt panel to generate enough electricity each day to run the pump for half an hour, assuming we're storing that electricity in a battery.

However, if you need continuous use of your device, you'll need a much larger panel. Let's say we're in a summer cabin in the woods and we want to run an oscillating fan to stay cool. We'll want to run it 24 hours though, because it's hot both during the day and at night while we're trying to sleep. A typical pedestal fan uses around 50 watts of power. Multiplied by 24 hours in a day, that's 1,200 watt hours, or 1.2 kWh of energy. That's a decent amount of electricity.

Now we'll have to make some assumptions and do some math again to determine how large of a solar panel we'll need. Assuming we're in an area with good sun, we can probably factor in 8 hours of solar power generation, meaning we'll need to generate enough energy in 8 hours to last for 24 hours, or in other words, 3x the amount of energy that we are using during the day. If we use 50 W for an hour to run the fan, that's 50 Wh. Multiply that by 3 and we have 150 Wh, or 150 watts of solar power generation for 8 hours straight, giving us 1,200 Wh (150 watts x 8 hours = 1,200 Wh).

But we can't just use a 150 W solar panel because it will never really produce 150 W. If we had a 200 W panel though, and it produced 75% of its rated power, we'd get our 150 W that we need. If we had a 300 W panel, it could produce enough electricity for us even if it only created half the power it is rated for. Both a 200 W or a 300 W panel could work in this situation, it just depends how strong the sun is in your area and how much you want to take a risk of sporadic cloud cover cutting into your power.

Let's stay on the safe side and say we'll choose a 300 W panel. That will also give us some wiggle room for some power being lost due to inefficiencies. We could get a single 300 W panel, but that would be pretty big, at approximately 15 square feet. Three 100 W panels would be more manageable, each setup next to each other to create a 300 W total solar panel array. Assuming these are 12 V panels (actually generating closer to 18-20 V open circuit), then we could connect all three in parallel and run the wire to a cheap PWM charge controller connected to a 12 V battery setup. (If you skipped Chapter 3 which introduced components including charge controllers and inverters, make sure you go back and read up on what those components are and how they are used).

We'll need to make sure our charge controller can handle this load though, so a charge controller rated for at least 300 W is required. At 12 V, that charge controller should be rated for at least 25 A, but 30 A would give us a slightly larger safety factor.

In order to properly size our battery, we'll need to know how long we plan to run our system without solar power being generated, i.e., how long we'll be running on battery power alone. In this example, we planned for 8 hours of solar power generation, leaving 16 hours of battery power. Since the PWM charge controller has a battery port and a load port, we will plug the inverter into the load port and the battery into the battery port. That means our 8 hours of fan run time during the day comes straight from the charge controller connected to the solar panels and not from the battery. The 16 hours of battery power needs to be sufficient for a 50 W load, meaning 800 Wh of energy (16 hours x 50 watts = 800 watt hours).

For a 12 V battery, 800 watt hours requires approximately 67 Ah. For a lead acid battery, we can't run it down below 50% though without compromising its health and longevity, so we need to plan for closer to 135 Ah for lead acid acid batteries. For lithium-ion batteries, we can basically discharge them to empty, though leaving a little bit left is still better for their health. Therefore, something around 75 Ah would be appropriate for a lithium-ion battery setup.

Assuming this is a 110 or 220 VAC fan instead of a 12 VDC fan, we'll need an inverter too. Our inverter will also have some losses due to inefficiencies, probably in the neighborhood of 10%. So instead of a 67 Ah battery at minimum, we'd probably need to start with a 12 V battery with an amp hour rating in the low 70's for lithium-ion batteries or at least 150 Ah for lead acid batteries.

This last example of a cabin fan is a bit of a hybrid between a small scale solar project and a small off-grid setup. This particular case with one load is just about as simple as an off-grid setup can be. We'll learn more about off-grid setups in Chapter 9, including more complicated setups with many loads.

Small components

From wiring to fuses, there are a number of small but important components that will play critical roles in your projects. Make sure you pay attention to the details to ensure you're using the correct components for your needs.

Wiring

Once you've chosen the parts for your solar setup, you're going to need to wire everything together. Most small scale solar projects are going to be mobile, meaning they're meant to get tossed in a backpack, packed in a suitcase or stuffed in the trunk of a car at some point. Anytime you're building something that is designed to move around or stand up to bending or vibrations, you should use stranded wire. Unlike solid wire, which is just one long chunk of metal, usually copper, in an insulated jacket, stranded wire consists of many thinner strands of metal conductors, usually twisted, inside of the insulation. Solid wire can handle more current, but it doesn't hold up to repeated bending or shaking well. Over time, this can cause wire fatigue. Stranded wire can resist damage due to motion for much longer than solid wire. However, stranded wire can't carry as much power as solid wire, so you need to use a slightly thicker stranded wire than solid wire.

Projects like USB chargers and other small projects that have charging cables usually experience the highest levels of movement and bending due to being stuffed in all kinds of pockets, bags and other tight places. If you've ever cut open a charging cable, you've probably seen that it is made of stranded wire with a very high strand count. The higher the strand count, the better the resistance is to failing during motion or bending. For these types of devices, I like to use high strand count silicone wire, which is meant for both high heat and high vibration environments, like in vehicles. With many dozens or even hundreds of individual strands, it costs more than cheap low strand count wire, but it really holds up versus wire with just a few individual strands.

Electrical connectors

Wire connectors come in all shapes and sizes. Many commercial solar panels come with MC4 style waterproof connectors, or other waterproof connectors. These are robust connectors that are specifically designed for these solar applications.

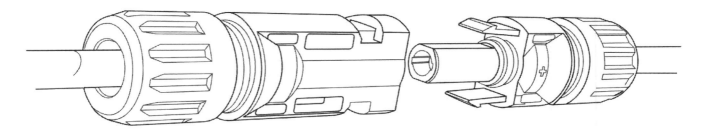

MC4 connectors commonly available on solar panels

For smaller projects though, many solar panels come with either clamp style connectors, like on a pair of automotive battery jumper cables, or no connectors at all. Clamp style connectors are often meant to clamp directly onto battery terminals, but can be fairly high resistance connections due to the small amount surface area actually making contact. I rarely use these clamp style connectors for anything other than testing. Other higher quality power transmitting electrical connectors common in the electronics industry are Anderson PowerPoles, XT30/XT60/XT90, Deans, and gold plated bullet connectors. None of these are inherently waterproof, but all can be covered in silicone, heat shrink or other similar coverings to add some level of water resistance.

General purpose electrical connectors

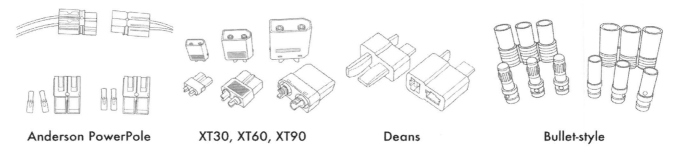

Anderson PowerPole   XT30, XT60, XT90   Deans   Bullet-style

It is important to choose the proper level of connector for a job based on its current rating. Generally speaking, you always want to use a larger rated connector than necessary. If I need to pass 15 A through a connection, then I'd want to use a connector rated for more than 15 A. In theory it might sound fine to use a 15 A connector for a 15 A circuit, but it is not advisable. This is because the ratings are usually made under perfect conditions. A lack of air flow, a less than ideal crimp or solder joint, or a number of other possibilities can lower the true current carrying ability of a connector. For these reasons, you should always use an electrical connector rated for more current than you plan to pass through the connector.

Electrical switches

The same can be said for switches. If you have a 10 A load, then using a 10 A switch will mean that the switch is pushed to its limit and more likely to fail. Remember that many of these small, inexpensive electronics components are mass produced for the cheapest price. Anything you can do to avoid overstressing a switch is advisable. I generally try to leave at least a 50% safety factor for most switches. Therefore, I would use a 15 A rated switch for a 10 A load.

Meters

Depending on your small scale solar project, being able to check on the capacity of your battery and the power flow in your system might be more or less important. Usually, a simple battery voltage gauge will be enough for most small projects. The voltage of a battery decreases as it is used, so a simple voltmeter gauge can give an approximation of the charge level of the battery. It is important to choose a voltmeter gauge that is calibrated for either lead acid or lithium-ion batteries, as they are not interchangeable. Also, lithium-ion voltmeter gauges might be preprogrammed for a certain number of cells in series or programmable to work on multiple custom sized batteries. Be sure to choose the correct one for your needs.

For more exact data than simple battery capacity approximations based on voltage levels, a power meter can be handy. DC watt meters are available with four wires for easy connections: a pair of red and black wires on the current in (source) side of the meter and a second pair on the current out (load) side of the meter. These meters can measure the exact battery capacity and voltage, but also show other useful information such as instantaneous power usage, total energy usage, peak power draw and more. These statistics can be helpful in determining how well your system is functioning, and whether your components are properly sized for the job.

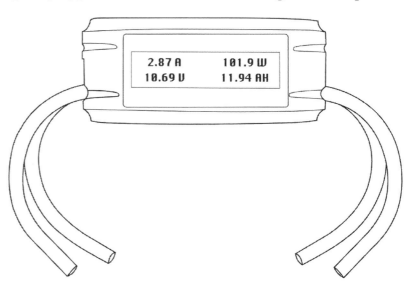

Internal shunt style DC wattmeter

Fuses

Fuses and circuit breakers are important safety devices that should be included in most solar power systems. The larger your system and the more power you're transferring, the more likely fuses will be necessary.

Fuses are often used to protect important parts of your system from damage in the event that something should go wrong, usually due to a short circuit. A short circuit can cause sudden spikes in current that can damage sensitive components.

For very small systems, fuses likely aren't necessary. If you have a little 6 V USB charger hooked up to a solar panel, there's not a lot that can go wrong. If the solar panel breaks, it will simply stop providing a current flow. If the charger connector breaks, current won't flow either. Simple.

The problem is more apparent on larger setups. Imagine if you had four solar panels connected in parallel. Damage to one panel could cause a short circuit where the current from the other three solar panels flows through the damaged panel. In this case, a fuse in line with each solar panel can prevent this from happening.

Another important case, which is more relevant for small solar projects like those in this chapter, is fusing at the battery. If you have a DC load connected to the battery and that DC load somehow experiences a failure, like a pump that seizes and causes a short circuit, you could see a huge spike in current being drawn from your battery. This can cause a fire hazard due to melting wires in a lead acid battery setup or a directly exploding battery in a lithium-ion battery setup. The solution here is to add a fuse in-line with the battery. When the high current is suddenly drawn, a fuse can blow and open the circuit, protecting your battery or wires from overheating.

Generally speaking, the fuse is chosen to be large enough that it won't blow from normal high-end use, but small enough that it will quickly blow from a short circuit. If I needed to power a 12 VDC light string that used 5 A, then a 10 A or 15 A fuse would probably suffice, chosen to be rated for a voltage larger than my voltage, which is 12 VDC in this case. It should never blow under normal working conditions of just 5 A, but a short circuit would likely pull more than 10-15 A, which should blow the fuse and protect my circuit.

The exact type and current rating of the fuse will depend on your specific needs, and should be chosen accordingly.

In some cases, you might want to use a circuit breaker instead of a fuse. Circuit breakers are like reusable fuses - they can be reset after tripping due to a current spike. If you have a system that will have common current spikes, such as what happens often with electric motor driven devices, it could be helpful to use a breaker instead of a fuse so that you don't have to replace burned fuses often. If you happen to be using a large device on the same circuit while the motor in your fridge's compressor turns on, a circuit breaker can trip to protect the circuit without requiring you to replace the part, as would be necessary with a blown fuse.

A common use for a breaker is after an AC-DC inverter. If you plug in too many devices to an AC-DC inverter and attempt to pull too much power, you could damage it. Most inverters should have over-current protection built-in, but it is a good idea not to risk it. A breaker can be chosen with a sufficient rating to trip once you get near the current limit on the inverter. This will serve as a safety device and reminder once you've approached the current limit that your inverter can handle. You could use a fuse here too and accomplish the same protection, but that would add the hassle and cost of needing to replace the fuse each time it blew.

Small solar projects that aren't handling much power can usually get away with minimal or no fuses at all. For larger projects, however, you should consider where in their circuits they need protection against overcurrent and short circuits, then choose sufficiently rated fuses to protect those areas.

Chapter 7: Large scale solar power for the home

When many people think of solar power, they think of a home with solar panels on the roof. This is one of the most common uses for solar power, and it makes a lot of sense. Our roofs spend all day baking in the sun, why not put them to use generating electricity?

Preparing for a home solar power system is not a small undertaking. It requires detailed planning, calculations and budget considerations. We'll cover all of those issues in this chapter.

Calculating solar energy needs

The first thing you'll need to consider is the energy requirement of your home. This is absolutely critical if you plan on installing an off-grid solar system because you won't have the local electrical grid to rely on if you run out of power by not preparing for all of your energy needs. If you plan on installing a grid-tie system though, then this isn't as critical, since you can always draw more power from the grid, but it is still important to understand.

To prepare for powering your home with solar energy, you'll need to do an energy audit of your home. This involves calculating the energy used by all of your devices. For a small cabin, this can be fairly straightforward. For a large home with many hundreds of devices, this can be a daunting task.

To make this process easier, a good place to start is with your electricity bill. It should show your total monthly energy usage, usually measured in kWh. You can use this to determine your average daily usage. For example, if your monthly kWh usage is 900 kWh, then dividing this number by 30 days in a month gives you 30 kWh of energy used per day. It's a good idea to go back at least a year and check all of your electrical bills, as your energy use can vary depending on the season.

If you don't have an electrical bill to use to gauge your energy use, such as if you're planning a new construction project or you're adding an off-grid setup to a cabin, RV or other building that doesn't currently have a connection to an electrical grid, you'll have to calculate your energy use manually. This entails adding up the energy used by each device and accounting for how often the device is used.

Most electrical devices should have a data plate or sticker on them somewhere that lists the current or wattage used by the device. A fan might use 50 watts and a hair dryer might use 1,800 watts. This is the instantaneous power used by the device. To determine the total energy used by the device, you'll need to multiply the power use in watts by the hours the device is in use. A 50 W fan that runs for 24 hours straight will use 1,200 watt-hours in a day, while the 1,800 watt hair dryer that only runs for 5 minutes (5 minutes = 0.0833 hours) will use just 150 watt-hours in a day.

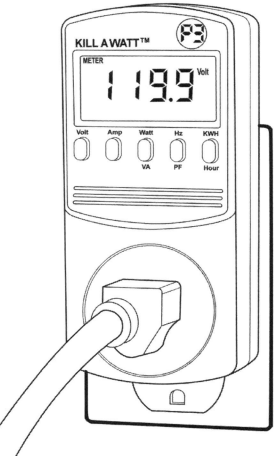

To obtain a more exact measurement of the instantaneous power and total energy used by the device, you can plug it into a meter known as a Kill-a-Watt meter. This is a handy device that measures the power and energy used by any AC electrical appliance. Simply plug the device into the Kill-a-Watt meter, then plug the Kill-a-Watt meter into the wall. The meter will calculate the exact instantaneous power usage of the device and will also measure the total energy used by the device over time.

By adding up the total watt-hours of every device you plan to use during the day, you can determine the total daily energy use of your home. Sometimes, it might be better to calculate energy use over a longer period. For example, some devices like vacuum cleaners, washing machines or blenders might not get used every day. If you use each device 2-3 times a week, then it might be more useful to calculate your weekly energy usage to account for these sporadically used devices.

By determining your total energy usage, you'll know how much energy you need to be able to store in your batteries (if you are planning an off-grid solar system) and/or how much energy you need to generate from solar panels each day (for both on and off-grid systems).

In addition to knowing your total energy usage, you'll also need to determine how much power you plan to use at one time. For example, many devices consume very little power, such as fans, light bulbs and chargers. However, if you plan to operate a few fans, dozens of light bulbs and a handful of chargers, your power use will quickly increase. Add into that mix more power hungry devices like kitchen appliances, heaters and air conditioning units, etc., and you can see how power usage can suddenly spike.

When you are connected to the grid, you have a nearly limitless supply of power being pumped into your home, so you don't have to worry too much about peak power usage, unless it is so high that you are tripping your circuit breakers out of danger of melting your wiring and circuitry.

However, for a home solar system where your power is limited by your batteries, solar panels and inverters, your power is certainly not infinite. Drawing higher power requires larger and more expensive batteries and/or inverters, and thus it can be beneficial to plan accordingly in order to reduce your peak power use.

A 3,000 W inverter is a decently large inverter, but a 1,500 W microwave and an 1,800 W hair dryer used at the same time can be enough to trip the circuit breaker protecting that 3,000 W inverter. For this reason, you'll want to make sure your components are rated for the power you'll use at any given time.

To determine your peak power requirements, list all of your devices along with their wattages, then determine which appliances could theoretically be used at the same time. Adding up their total wattages will determine your maximum peak power requirement. By understanding how this maximum peak power works, you can think about which devices you want to use together and which you should wait to use. A 4,000 W inverter is significantly more expensive than a 3,000 W inverter, so it might just make more sense to wait to microwave your popcorn until your wife finishes using her hair dryer.

That being said, most inverters will have two ratings: a maximum continuous power rating and a peak power rating. The maximum continuous power rating is the amount of power that the inverter can supply all day, every day, without a problem. The maximum peak power rating is the amount of surge power the inverter can handle. Different inverters use different rating systems for this number. Some indicate that the surge rating can be supported for 30 seconds while others say 5 minutes. You'll need to verify this for each inverter you consider in order to make the appropriate choice. For example, if the 5-minute surge rating for a 3,000 W continuous inverter is 5,000 W, then you can run that 1,800 W hair dryer and 1,500 W microwave at the same time for a short period of time. In this case, as long as you only need a couple minutes to microwave your popcorn, you can do it even while the hair dryer is running.

So now you can see why it is best to try and stagger the use of high power devices to reduce the load on your system at any given time, but this same principle is also important for reducing the total energy load on the system as well, especially for off-grid systems where your total energy in storage is a finite amount. If you plan to use the washing machine, vacuum cleaner, and treadmill all on the same day, you could end up with a large amount of your total weekly energy use all occurring in a short period of time. This would require a larger battery bank to provide that much energy in a single day. However, if you did laundry one day, vacuumed the next and then ran on the treadmill on the third day, you'd spread out your energy usage and reduce the total energy usage per day. That would mean you could get away with a smaller battery bank that gets refilled each day for the next day's use, instead of needing to store so much extra energy for use all in a single day.

Obviously every home and every person will have a different idea of what "a lot" of energy use is. For a self sufficient person living in an off-grid hunting cabin, 2,000 watt-hours a day might be plenty to provide for a simple life. For a family of five that enjoys many more indulgences inside of their large home, 2,000 watt-hours might not last an hour. But knowing your total energy and power use, whatever it is, is the first step to planning your solar-powered home.

Reducing home energy usage

After doing your energy audit and determining how much energy you use, your eyes might be rolling back in your head. It's one thing to use a lot of energy when there's a tap in the wall for an unlimited supply. It's another thing when you have to generate and store all of that energy yourself. That is why one of the most important steps for planning a solar powered home is actually reducing the total energy use in the home.

This is a lot easier than most people think, largely because most people waste more energy than they realize. By looking for a number of common energy wasting sources, you can easily make a large dent in your total energy usage, which will not only reduce the money you spend on electricity, but also the investment in all of your solar power equipment.

Go easy on your heating and cooling

Air conditioners are usually the single largest usage of electricity in the entire home. If you generate heat from electricity as well, then that might be the second largest energy consumer in your home. When you have unlimited energy, it's easier to crank up the air conditioning and forget about it, even knowing that you are paying for it at the end of the month. When your batteries are going to run dry soon though, suddenly it makes a lot more sense to be reasonable.

In the summer, try wearing less clothing and make sure it is fabric that breathes. In the winter, bundle up a bit more. You don't have to walk around your home naked or in a jacket (unless you want to, and that's your prerogative) but by dressing more appropriately for the season, you don't have to spend as much energy turning your home into an artificial environment. Make sure you're replacing the filters in your air conditioning unit as well. An old filter will cause your air conditioning unit to work even harder, burning more energy.

Keeping window curtains closed on any windows that face the sun can make a big improvement for air conditioning bills. Going a step further, planting shrubbery and bushes on the sunny side of the house keeps the house from baking and heating up further.

Use a fan instead of the air conditioner when you can. My wife is a bit more finicky in the summer than I am, but when it's just me at home, I turn off the air conditioning and use a fan in whatever room I'm sitting in. A fan will often use less than 10% of the energy of an air conditioner. Just don't leave a fan on in a room in order to cool it off when you're not there - that doesn't work. Fans cool you off by using evaporative cooling. They move the warm boundary layer of air that sits around your body, bringing in new cool air and evaporating the slight amount of moisture on your skin. The air itself isn't any cooler, but moving air cools off your body through evaporation. If you're not in the room, moving air won't make the room any cooler than it was before. Fans have a cooling effect on humans, but don't actually cool air by themselves. So always turn them off when you're not around.

Reduce the use of heating appliances

Electric heaters are huge energy users. Anything with an electric heater built in can use a surprising amount of energy. When possible, wash your clothes with room temperature water or use one of the lowest heat settings.

Refrigerators and freezers are included in this category of heating appliances. Refrigerators and freezers are actually a big heater on one side, which is how it creates cold air on the other side, just like an air conditioning unit. That's why the outside unit of your air conditioner and the back of the fridge feel so hot. Make sure your refrigerator doors are always closed and sealed properly to keep them from running more than necessary. If your refrigerator or freezer has a poor seal in the door, it can easily use twice as much energy by running its compressor more often as cold air escapes.

Electric ovens also use a huge amount of energy. If possible, heat up food in the microwave instead of baking it in the oven. Even though a microwave might use twice as much power, the oven can take much longer to heat food, meaning the microwave actually uses less total energy per meal.

Make sure appliances that are off are really "off"

Most appliances, such as TVs, printers, laptop/phone chargers, etc., will still draw power when plugged in, even if they aren't being used. It can be annoying to unplug these devices all the time, but supplying multiple devices with a single power strip can make this easier by providing a single button on the power strip to switch off after use.

Also, instead of blindly unplugging everything, use a Kill-a-Watt meter like the one discussed earlier in this chapter to measure the power draw of devices when they are off but still plugged in. Your phone charger might be drawing just 10 milliwatts while your big TV might be drawing more than 10 watts while both are plugged in but turned off. In this case, unplugging the TV for just 1 hour will save as much energy as unplugging your phone charger for 1,000 hours. It obviously makes more sense to invest a bit of time and energy into determining which devices have larger power uses when off, and focus on disconnecting those larger offenders when not in use.

Save more energy in your kitchen

We already talked about refrigerators wasting energy through leaky seals, but there's even more ways you can save energy with your refrigerator. Use it to thaw foods by moving them from the freezer to the refrigerator instead of defrosting with an appliance.

But don't stop there. Look around your kitchen for more energy saving opportunities. When heating water on an electric range, use a cover to keep heat in and reduce cooking time. If your dishwasher has an economy cycle and your dishes aren't a complete disaster, use it! The economy cycle will save both water and energy. Also, only run your dishwasher when it is full. Running a partial load is a waste of energy. The same goes for your washing machine too!

By saving energy around your house, you are not only doing something good for the environment, you're also making it possible to save money on a more reasonable sized solar system. And there's nothing wrong with saving money!

Planning for solar panels

Now that you've determined your energy usage, peak power usage and hopefully reduced your total energy requirement with some energy efficient strategies, you're ready to plan for your solar panel setup.

The number of solar panels you'll need is determined by your total energy usage and the type of solar power system you're using, either grid-tie or off-grid. For grid-tie, you have a lot more freedom in determining how many solar panels to install. If you install only a few panels, you'll cut down on your electricity bill by generating some of your own electricity, but you likely won't cover all of your day time needs, meaning you'll still be buying some energy from the grid during the day. You can always add more panels as time goes on to increase your own energy production and decrease the amount of electricity you must buy from the grid.

For off-grid solar systems, it is much more important that you plan your solar panel numbers accordingly. Since you don't have the grid to fall back on, if you don't generate enough power from your solar panels, then your lights (and everything else) will go out. For this reason, most off-grid solar installations include a backup gasoline or diesel generator just in case. However, you want to avoid having to run such a generator as much as possible by planning to have enough solar panels in your system.

Similar to the calculations we made in Chapter 6 for small scale solar projects, you'll need to calculate how much power and energy you'll need your solar panels to generate. This is true for both on and off-grid systems, it's just more critical for off-grid systems.

You'll need to make some assumptions during these calculations, including how many hours a day you'll have good sunlight and how efficient your solar panels will be, meaning how much of the advertised power you'll really get. Different areas get different amounts of daily sunlight, and this changes with the seasons, so you'll need to lookup these values for your area. This is where a local solar power installer can be very helpful.

For example, let's consider an area that gets a conservative estimate of six hours of sunlight per day. Obviously the sun is out for more than six hours a day in most areas, but the first couple hours and last couple hours of the day aren't going to generate as much electricity, so a conservative estimate is usually safer.

To determine the total solar power needed, simply divide the daily energy requirement by the number of hours of power generation. If we know that our house needs 20 kWh of energy per day, and we want to generate that much energy in six hours, we'll need to divide 20 kWh of energy by six hours, giving us 3.333 kW, or 3,333 watts of power.

Realistically speaking though, solar panels don't achieve their full rated power under normal conditions. Many people will use a correction factor to estimate the actual, real world output of a solar panel. The real world output can vary considerably, and might be 80% in a really sunny area, or even less than 50% under poor daytime conditions. I will often use somewhere around two thirds, or 66.67%, which is usually fairly conservative. Depending on your area, your panels might produce more of their rated power than this though, so again, consulting a local solar power expert can be helpful.

Let's say that we are in a sunny area, and we'll get around 75% of our rated solar panel's output for those 6 hours of sun each day. To determine the actual rated wattage of solar panels we'll need, we can divide our power requirement by the expected amount of rated power that our solar panels should achieve, which we are calling 0.75, or 75%. Therefore, 3.333 kW divided by 0.75 gives us 4.444 kW, or 4,444 watts of power. Rounding up to a nice round number, we'll need a 4,500 W or 4.5 kW solar panel installation. If we are using 250 W panels, we'll need 18 panels total.

You'll notice that we made a number of assumptions here, and those assumptions will most likely be different for your project. Your area might get significantly more or less than 6 hours of sun per day, and your panels might do better or worse than 75% of their rated power. This example should be altered to fit your specific situation.

Another factor to consider is the difference in sun exposure during summer as compared to winter in your area. If you live near the equator, your total sun per day will remain fairly constant throughout the year. This means you should experience fairly consistent solar power generation. The farther you live from the equator, the less sun you'll get during the winter months. This will result in less solar power generation during the winter months. Depending on your needs, this could be either a small inconvenience or a big problem. For on-grid setups, less winter sun simply means you'll buy more electricity from the grid during those months as compared to during the summer. However, if you're planning an off-grid setup, you need to consider the winter sun carefully to ensure that you'll be generating enough electricity to meet your needs in the winter.

Once you have considered your home or building's total energy needs and have factored in seasonal sun exposure, you will be able to calculate how many solar panels you will need. Now we can begin planning how those solar panels will be arranged. We'll likely have strings and arrays, meaning we'll have both series and parallel circuits of solar panels. For a 12 VDC system, we'd need to use seriously heavy gauge wire to carry 4.5 kW of power. That wire would need to handle 375 amps. Consulting wire ampacity charts, we find that level to usually be off the chart.

If you have a lower power system, you might be able to get away with 12 VDC. This is useful for things like cabins that don't use much power and have short wire runs. For most homes though, you're going to be looking at a minimum of 24 VDC, and quite likely 48 VDC.

Let's look at our example here for both options. At 24 VDC, our 4,500 W system is pulling 187.5 A. This is a more reasonable amount, but still fairly large. At this level, for reasonable wire lengths we are still looking at 4/0 AWG wire based on wire ampacity charts. That wire is getting close to the thickness of your pinky and can be prohibitively expensive. But what if we went with a 48 VDC system? That would mean we'd only be dealing with approximately 94 A. Consulting wiring charts, we can see that we are now realistically into the 1-2 AWG size range, depending on wire length. This wire costs a fraction of the larger wire sizes. For the price difference, we could probably even afford a few more big solar panels.

You can consult wire charts like I do for looking up the amp rating of different wires over different lengths, but I recommend using an online calculator tool to make this process easier and avoid making mistakes. Renogy has great calculators for solar panel size, wire size and battery size at https://www.renogy.com/calculators/ and the calculators make estimating your needs in these areas much easier.

Back to our solar panel setup. If we are using 2 AWG wire, we can comfortably run 30 feet of wire to our inverter or our charge controller and batteries. For longer lengths, you'll need thicker wire due to the increased resistance of the additional wire length. If you can locate your inverter or charge controller and batteries closer to your solar panels, you'll save significantly on wire costs.

This shows us that a 48 V setup for our solar panels would be great, while a 24 V setup is less than ideal and a 12 V setup is impractical. With our 18 panels, we'll need to determine an arrangement that can produce 48 V. Many residential panels are 24 V panels (or closer to 30-36 V) open circuit), which means we could run two panels in series to reach 48 V. This two panel string would output closer to 70 V open circuit, which drops to around 56 V with a load. If we first create two sets of nine solar panels in parallel to create an array, we can then put those two sets in series to double the voltage from 24 V to 48V. The current will also be 9x higher than the current of a single panel.

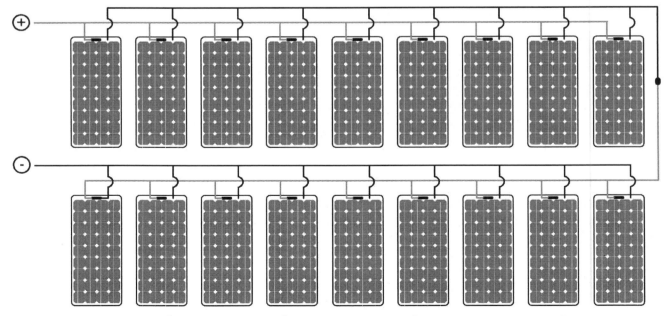

Two sets of nine 24V panel arrays connected in series to create 48V

You'd use this same process to achieve different voltages and currents for any system. If your inverter or charge controller can handle even higher voltage, then you could make strings of three panels instead of two, and then have six of those strings in parallel to achieve the same 18 total panels. This produces the same power, but with higher voltage and lower current.

Many inverters are capable of DC voltages of up to 400-600 VDC, meaning you can significantly reduce your current levels and wire thickness. Keep in mind though that such high voltage DC can be incredibly dangerous or even deadly if you don't know what you're doing. Those levels of DC voltage are best left to the professionals to install.

The arrangement of solar panels can vary depending on your requirements and the specifications of your solar equipment such as inverters and charge controllers. By adjusting the number of series and parallel panels, you'll be able to dial in the appropriate levels for your components and system.

Solar panel installation

The most common location for home solar panels is on the roof of your home. However, it is important to check your local building codes. There may be regulations on solar panel installations on residential buildings. The last thing you want is to buy a whole pile of panels only to determine that you aren't allowed to install them in the way you originally planned.

For roof mounted systems, it is highly recommended to consult with a solar electricity expert in your area who can help you plan the most efficient and cost effective setup for your particular house. With their experience, they can often save you money by helping you determine the best places to mount your panels and which places to avoid based on your particular roof angle, location and compass direction. A good way to get started on your own though is to use an online tool such as Project Sunroof from Google, which uses the shape and direction of your roof to help you plan out and calculate the benefits of solar panels on your roof and can connect you to local solar panel experts and installers.

Solar panels don't only have to be mounted on your roof. If you have the space, a location on the ground that doesn't get much shade can also be used for mounting solar panels. In the northern hemisphere, you'll want a location on the southern portion of your roof or house, and in the southern hemisphere, you'll want a location on the northern portion of your roof or house.

If you do choose to mount your solar panels on your roof, you need to ground them to protect from lightning strikes. All of the electronics connected to the solar panels, including the inverters and even your TV, can be damaged due to lightning strikes on or near ungrounded solar panel installations. With long cable runs, the lightning doesn't even have to be that close. Distant lightning can still induce large currents in long wire runs. Proper grounding procedures protect against this phenomenon and can prevent expensive damage to your electronics. Grounding also helps reduce electrical hum from devices like inverters and fluorescent lights, which will improve the quality and performance of your entire system.

To ground your solar panels, start by pounding a 6-foot copper grounding rod into the ground, leaving just a few inches showing above ground. A copper grounding rod can be purchased at most home improvement stores. Clamp a length of 6 AWG solid copper grounding wire to the grounding rod and run the grounding wire up to your solar panels. If all of your solar panels are connected to a conductive metal frame on your roof, then you can connect the copper grounding wire directly to the frame. If your solar panels are mounted on a wooden frame, you'll need to connect the individual metal frames of your solar panels together and then connect them to the copper grounding wire.

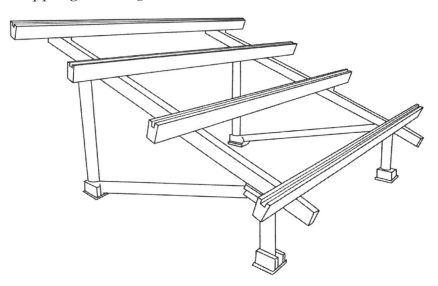

A simple ground mounted solar panel rack is easy to build

Roof mounted solar panels have the advantage of not taking up space in your yard, but can be difficult to access for periodic cleanings and adjustments. Ground-mounted solar panels, on the other hand, can be more easily cleaned and adjusted to better track the sun as the seasons change. Some solar panels are rigid mounted in frames and can't be adjusted. However, adjustable angle solar panel mounts can make your system more efficient. In the summer, you'll want your panels pointed higher up into the sky as the sun passes more vertically over them. In the winter, the sun is lower in the sky so you'll want your panels angled towards a point lower in the sky.

You don't have to go crazy with this. Some people build automated systems to track the sun across the sky during the day and up and down as the seasons change. For most people though, adjusting the angle of your solar panels once a month to a point higher or lower in the sky is plenty. And realistically speaking, non adjustable solar panels are just fine too. They don't eek out every last bit of solar power possible, but they still capture the lion's share of it.

When mounting solar panels on your roof, it is best to drill directly into roof rafters if possible. Depending on your frame, you might only be able to get one side of the frame to line up on a rafter. In this case, use toggle bolts on the side for extra security. After drilling the mounting holes in your roof, fill the holes with silicone caulk or roofing cement, then drive the screws into them. This will give the best watertight seal.

Screws with a neoprene rubber washer meant for roofing work should be used whenever drilling into the rafter. If using a toggle bolt in an area where you can't drill directly into a rafter, use a considerable amount of silicone caulk or roofing cement before and after inserting the toggle bolt.

To run the wires through the roof, you'll want to use a flashing boot designed to fit under your roof shingles. It looks like a large shingle with a rubber plunger in the middle. The hole at the center of the plunger will be sized for standard electrical conduit. This allows you to run electrical conduit through your roof in a waterproof manner.

Adjustable solar panel mounts can increase efficiency

Locate the boot underneath one of the panels to shield it from direct rain and ensure that the underside of the roof in that location is free of electrical wiring. Start by drilling a pilot hole through the roof with a small diameter drill bit. Then, once you've located the hole on the inside of the roof and now double-checked that you are away from any electrical wiring under the roof, use a hole saw or spade-tip bit that matches the size of your electrical conduit to cut a hole in the roof.

Slide the top edge of the boot's flashing under the shingles above it so that rain cascades down over the flashing like a standard roof tile. Install your conduit through the boot, bending the conduit where necessary. The outside end of the conduit should reach the underside of the last solar panel in your array and connect to a junction box at that point where the wiring can feed down through the conduit and into your house.

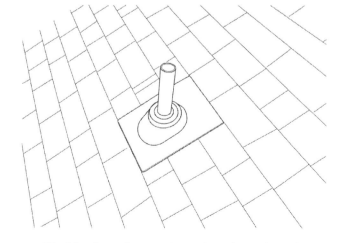

At this point, the wiring will vary depending on the components used in your system. These will vary between on and off-grid systems, so we'll cover each in more detail in the next two chapters.

Flashing boot for running wires through roof

Chapter 8: Grid-tie solar

Note: if you're skipping around in this book and not reading in order, make sure you read Chapter 7 on planning for a solar powered home, and preferably before you read this chapter. It contains important preliminary information relevant to a grid-tie solar setup.

Grid-tie solar power is a great way to get into solar power use at home with either a small or large scale system. With grid-tie solar, you don't need to worry about any issues related to energy storage, meaning you can forget all about batteries, which are usually the most expensive part of any solar powered system.

What is grid-tie solar?

As we discussed in the overview in Chapter 3, grid-tie solar systems have a direct connection between the solar panels that power the home and the local electrical grid. Grid-tie solar systems can be large or small, functioning much the same way regardless of size.

The reason grid-tie solar is a great way to ease into solar electricity generation at home is that you don't need to start off by producing enough electricity to power your home. With grid-tie systems, you can obtain electricity both from your solar panels and the local electrical grid at the same time.

If you only have a few solar panels, you'll use all of the electricity that they are generating during the day, and you'll draw any extra electricity you need from the local power grid. In this way, the solar panels cut down on the amount of electricity you draw from the grid, which cuts down on your electricity bill too. At night, your solar panels aren't going to generate any electricity of course, so you'll be drawing all of your electricity from the grid.

Over time you can add more solar panels to your system, which will increase the amount of solar energy your house is using and decrease the amount of grid energy you have to buy from the electrical company. Because solar panel prices have been steadily decreasing over the last few years, this can be a good way to hedge your investment in solar for the future. You can invest in the more expensive electronic components now and only buy a few solar panels at first, then add more solar panels in the coming years as the price of the panels continues to drop.

Eventually, you may end up with enough solar panels that you're generating more electricity during the day than you actually use. This is known as an energy surplus. Because grid-tie systems don't have batteries for energy storage, this electricity can often be sold back to the electric company to feed to other homes on the grid. This net metering causes your meter to run backwards during the day. Laws differ around the country and world, and many areas have begun to regulate net metering by reducing the value of the electricity sold back to the grid or outlawing it altogether. However, if net metering is available in your area, it can be a great way to save even more money on solar by getting energy 'credits' from the electrical company for surplus energy during the day and then buying the electricity that you use from the grid at night with those same credits.

While grid-tie solar has many advantages, it does have one distinct disadvantage. If there's ever a power outage due to the grid failing, such as during a storm or cyber attack, you're out of power as well unless you can generate enough to be sufficient during the day. Then at night you're totally out of power, since you don't have a way to store the energy you generate during the day. Even so, this disadvantage is rare enough that most people who use grid-tie solar systems don't seem to mind, especially when they see how much money they save by not buying batteries!

Necessary components

We briefly discussed the components used in grid-tie solar systems in the subject's overview in Chapter 3. Now we can go into further detail on some of the components we haven't yet discussed as thoroughly.

Solar panels

Obviously you're going to need a solar panel array. The size and number will need to be determined based on your needs and budget, which we discussed in Chapter 7 on planning for home solar installations. As described in Chapter 5, your main two options for solar panels for a large grid-tie or off-grid system include polycrystalline and monocrystalline solar panels. Polycrystalline solar panels are a bit cheaper, but aren't as efficient so you need more of them. Monocrystalline panels are slightly more expensive, but you can generate more electricity in somewhat less space. In the end, the price difference usually works out to nearly zero, so the bigger issue is often space.

Inverter

A grid-tie inverter is the magical piece of equipment that converts the DC electricity generated by your solar panels into the AC electricity used in your home. There are actually a few different types of inverters that you can use for grid-tie systems.

The first type of inverter is a standard grid-tie inverter, also known as a string inverter because it is connected to a string (or series connection) of solar panels. This is the simplest type of inverter and is the most commonly used inverter for grid-tie applications. It receives the DC electricity generated by your solar panels and converts it into AC electricity like a standard inverter, and then it plugs into your home's electrical grid, either at any electrical outlet in the home or directly at the AC breaker box.

While plugging the output of a grid-tie inverter into any electrical outlet in the home will work to power your home, it might not meet the electric codes in your area. Many countries will require a dedicated circuit in your AC breaker box for grid-tie AC power. Check your local laws to see if this applies to your area.

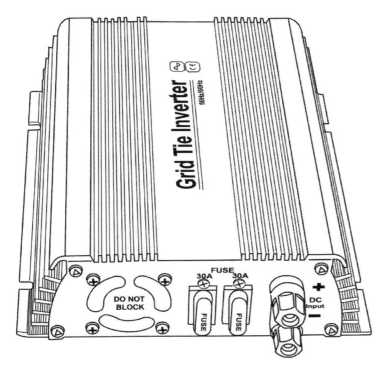

Additionally, there are cases where plugging a grid-tie inverter into a standard outlet in your home can even be dangerous. The AC circuit breakers in your home are set to trip when you are drawing more current than the wires can handle. But if you are putting power into that circuit from a plug-in grid-tie inverter, it is possible to pull more current from that circuit than the circuit breaker should allow, since the amount of current drawn only from the grid (which the circuit breaker senses) might still be a safe level, but the total being drawn, including the additional current from the plug-in grid-tie inverter, might be more than the wiring in the circuit can handle. This could cause a disastrous fire in your wall. For this reason, most areas require a grid-tie inverter to be wired to its own circuit with a dedicated circuit breaker and not share a circuit like plug-in grid-tie inverters typically do.

One of the main drawbacks of a string inverter is that if one solar panel in the string gets obscured, all solar panels in the string will have their power reduced to the level of the obscured panel, and the inverter will receive less total power. This can happen due to shade from a nearby tree, bird droppings, snow cover, a frisbee landing on the roof, etc. When one solar panel in a string gets partially blocked, the result to the string inverter is as if all of the solar panels are partially blocked.

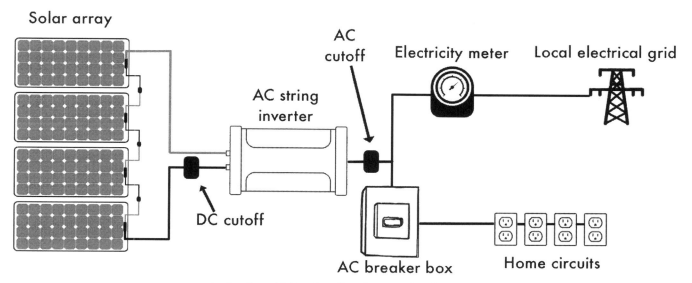

A simple grid-tie circuit using a string inverter

The second type of inverter is a dual purpose grid-tie inverter that also includes a built-in charge controller. This inverter functions like a normal grid-tie inverter in that it feeds AC electricity into your home and back to your local electrical grid if you generate a surplus, but it also functions like an off-grid inverter in that it connects to a battery bank to source and invert DC electricity, allowing you to pull AC electricity directly from the inverter.

In addition, the built in charge controller means you do not need a separate charge controller. However, these inverter/charge controller combos are both more expensive and harder to find. Don't worry though, you can still achieve this hybrid grid-tie-with-battery setup simply by using a dual purpose inverter coupled with a charge controller.

This dual setup is meant for a hybrid system where you are grid-tied but also want to store energy in your own battery bank to avoid selling surplus energy back to the grid. This can be helpful if you live in an area that doesn't allow net metering, meaning you can't sell your surplus electricity back for a fair price.

Keep in mind though that with this hybrid setup, the issue of solar panel strings being partially obscured and reducing power to the inverter applies in this case as well.

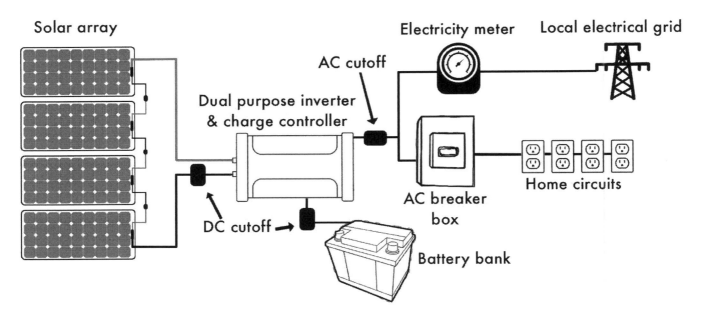

A hybrid grid-tie circuit using a dual purpose inverter/charge controller

The third type of inverter is a microinverter. Instead of one single large inverter that collects the electricity from all of your solar panels, microinverters are mounted on the back of each solar panel and perform the DC to AC conversion right at the source, before the electricity enters your home. The advantages of microinverters are that they allow each solar panel to operate independently. That means that if a single panel is obscured, the other panels continue working at full power. This is unlike a standard inverter system, where all the panels are connected in DC strings and arrays before reaching the inverter, meaning that a single panel being covered by shade or debris will reduce the power of all the other solar panels in the system.

Microinverters are also somewhat safer, since you don't have high power DC electricity entering your home. The conversion to AC occurs right at the solar panel, meaning you are working with safer AC electricity in your home. Microinverters do tend to be a bit more expensive though, as they are a newer technology and require one microinverter for every solar panel in your setup.

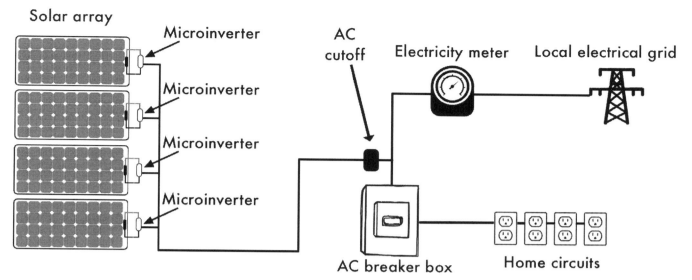

A simple microinverter-based grid-tie circuit

As discussed previously in this chapter, grid-tie solar systems allow you to start with a few solar panels and expand your system by adding more panels in the future. If this is your plan, and if you are using a standard grid-tie or dual purpose inverter, it is often recommended to invest as much as you can in a powerful inverter first, so that it will be robust enough for a larger solar panel array in the future without having to buy new, larger components when you eventually add more solar panels.

DC junction box

If you aren't using microinverters, you'll likely need to include a DC junction box. This is installed before the inverter and is usually located near or behind one of the solar panels. The purpose of the DC junction box is to receive the multiple solar panel strings and combine them. It may also house the fuses and a DC cut-off switch to cut power coming from the solar panels. Most industrialized countries have laws that require residential electrical connections to be made inside of a closed junction box - you can't simply tape wires together and leave them hanging around on your roof somewhere.

Many areas also require a manual DC disconnect switch on grid-tied solar panel installations. Others require an automatic DC disconnect switch. In some cases, the on/off switch on your grid-tie inverter might fulfill this requirement. Check with your local building codes or authorities. In the event that it does not fulfill a local requirement, you'll need to include an appropriate DC disconnect switch.

AC breaker box

Your home already has an AC breaker box, but you will most likely need to make some modifications to it for your grid-tie solar installation. The grid-tie inverter should output AC voltage to your AC breaker box where it is fed into your home's circuits. Many national electric codes require this to be on a separate, independent AC circuit within your breaker box. Even if your local laws don't require this, it is a very good idea and highly recommended. This is a safety issue that prevents a circuit from pulling more current than its wiring can support, which can happen if a grid-tie inverter is plugged into an existing AC circuit shared by multiple other loads.

Also, remember that connections made inside of your home's AC breaker box should only be attempted by those with the proper training. If you don't feel confident doing this work (or it is against your local building codes), be sure to have a certified electrician help you or perform the work for you. AC can kill.

Electricity meter

For grid-tie systems, you'll usually need to replace your electricity meter in your home for one that is compatible with power flowing in both directions. This is usually a job for your local electrical company, and they often provide the new power meter for free. If they don't provide you with one or perform the installation for you, check with them to make sure that you are purchasing a net meter that is approved for their system. And with any luck, you're in an area that allows net-metering so you can sell your electricity back to the power company at full price.

Fuses and breakers

Fuses and breakers will be required at different locations to protect the expensive electronics and components in your solar power system. It is important to size these correctly for the job. For example, you likely need a much larger current fuse on the heavy gauge wires that connect your solar panels to your inverter due to the high current. If you have current lower than 100 to 125 amps, you can probably find a resettable circuit breaker to perform this function. Above those current levels, you'll need to use a heavy duty fuse. Here's a tip: high quality heavy duty fuses can often be found from boat and marine parts vendors.

In comparison, a much lower current breaker can be used on the output side of your inverter. At that point, you'll be using higher voltage AC, meaning your current will be reduced, often by as much as 5 to 10 times compared to the higher current DC from the solar panels.

Design and setup

Your solar panel installation will follow the methods detailed in Chapter 7, where we also covered the design of the series and parallel layout of the panels and the wiring size selection (hint: online wire calculators are your friend). Whether you're using rooftop or ground level solar panels, the basic installation process is the same: a sturdy frame and well grounded panels are essential.

As we've already covered the physical installation, we'll start here with the electrical side of things. Your first step will be wiring your panels either to a DC junction box en route to your grid-tie inverter or wiring your panels directly to microinverters. Microinverters make the job simpler, but remember that they are a bit more expensive.

If you're working with microinverters, mount one to each of your solar panels. They are waterproof, but hiding them under your panel adds more protection and helps keep the wire mess out of the way as well. The microinverter will have DC connectors that connect to the positive and negative DC connectors on your solar panel. It will also have another AC connector that plugs into a main AC line that runs between the panels.

Many microinverter systems also having extra monitoring capabilities that allow you to track the performance of each panel. In these systems, the microinverter might have another connector, or this data connection could be handled by a single AC connector with multiple extra data pins.

Many microinverters will also have a metal shell to allow for grounding as well. In this case, a grounding wire can be mounted behind the solar panels and connect to each microinverter. This grounding wire can usually be shared by the solar panels and the microinverters.

Depending on the number of solar panels you have in your system, you might need more than one AC circuit. If this is the case, you'll run additional AC lines just like the first one, passing under each panel and connecting each microinverter. Many areas have codes requiring certain electrical conduit specifications for your wire runs. Make sure to check your local ordinances for any specific and relevant codes.

From here, you'll run your AC line(s) to a junction box. This will join the copper grounding wire to the AC bus ground as well as your 120 or 240 VAC wires and communication wire for your microinverters. It is important to have your ground connected properly inside of the junction box and and to use whichever electrical conduit is required by your area.

At this point you will continue your AC wires down to your main AC panel on the outside of your home. Before entering your main AC panel, the AC wires will first enter a separate junction box housing an AC disconnect. From the AC disconnect, your AC wiring, including the grounding wire, will continue on to the main AC panel. It is highly advisable to have a certified electrician install this portion of the wiring, and may be required by law in some areas. The AC input from your solar panels should receive its own dedicated breaker inside the main AC panel, and might require multiple if you have a large number of panels.

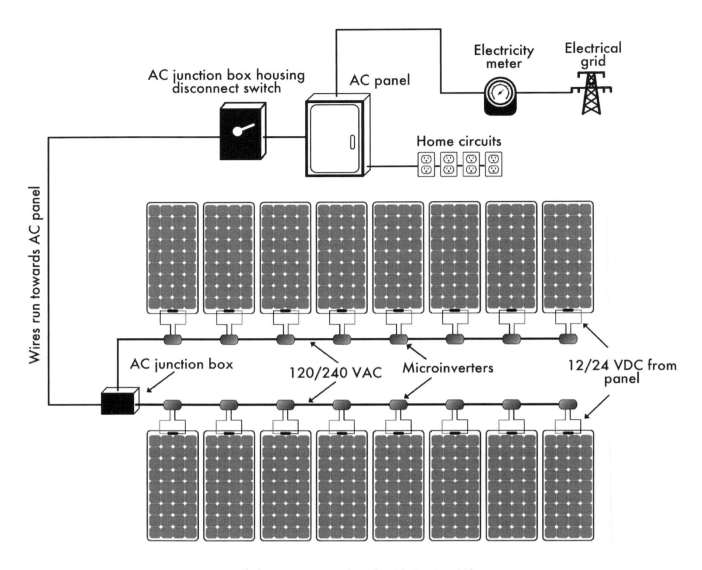

Detailed microinverter-based grid-tie circuit layout

If you aren't using microinverters, then you'll likely have one or more string inverters. The design and setup process is similar, but lacks the optimization at each panel that microinverters provide. For a string inverter system, you'll begin by running the DC wires in series to create your string of solar panels, which as we discussed, will add the voltage of each panel while keeping the current of the entire string equal to the current of a single panel in the string.

From here, you'll run your DC wiring down to your inverter, including a DC disconnect before your inverter to allow you to shut off and disconnect the solar panels from the system. From the disconnect, your positive and negative DC wires will plug into your grid-tie inverter. If you are using multiple string inverters, you will have multiple connections and multiple DC disconnects before each inverter.

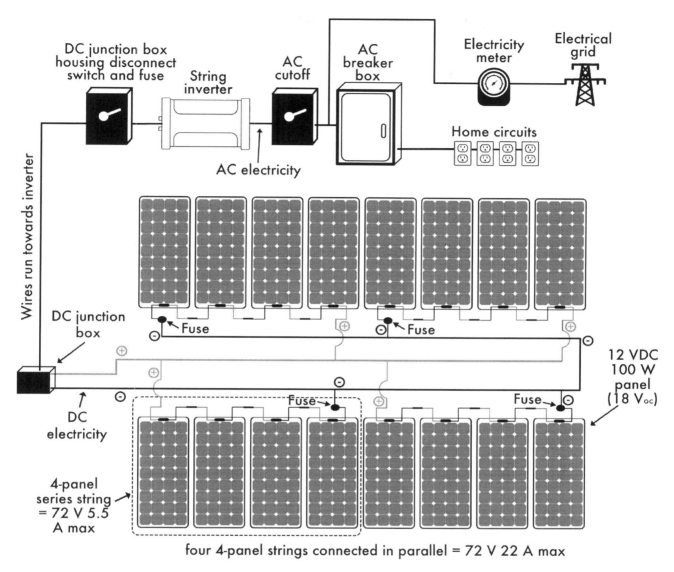

Detailed string inverter-based grid-tie circuit layout

Having multiple strings of solar panels doesn't always mean that you need multiple string inverters. If your inverter can handle the power of multiple strings wired in parallel to make a larger array, then you can definitely use that option. Just remember that if you have multiple strings wired in parallel, usually three or more, then you'll want to make sure each is fused to prevent a short circuit in one string from damaging the others.

Your inverter will then be connected to your main AC panel, where the input should be placed on its own independent circuit with its own appropriately sized breaker. Again, this step is best left to professional electricians. Messing around inside your main AC panel can be dangerous if you don't know what you are doing.

The last option is to use one or more plug-in grid tie inverters, which don't require accessing your main AC panel. This method will begin just as in the previous method with your DC wires running down to your inverter with a DC disconnect between the panels and the inverter. Then you'll plug your inverter into an AC outlet in your home. Many people will use a Kill-a-watt meter in this outlet as a way to monitor the output of the solar panels.

While this method will work, remember that many areas don't allow the use of these plug-in grid inverters because they don't have an independent circuit connected via your main AC panel. Therefore, be sure to research beforehand and determine whether this method is legal for your area. If it is, be sure to avoid overloading whichever circuit into which you plug your grid-tie inverter. With the addition of a grid-tie inverter, that circuit will be capable of providing more power than it was originally designed to handle, and the AC panel's circuit breaker might not blow when the circuit reaches its maximum safe current because less power will be passing through the panel and circuit breaker from the grid, despite more power flowing in the circuit due to the addition of the grid-tie inverter.

As we discussed earlier in this chapter, grid-tie systems are a great way to get your feet wet with solar power without having to make a large up front investment. If you're ready for the big leagues though and want to cut the cord to the electrical company altogether, then the only answer is to go off-grid. That's what we'll be covering in the next chapter.

Chapter 9: Off-grid solar

Note: if you're skipping around in this book and not reading in order, make sure you read Chapter 7 on planning for a solar powered home, and preferably before you read this chapter. It contains important preliminary information relevant to an off-grid solar power setup. I also recommend reading Chapter 8 on grid-tie systems, since many of the same components are used in both systems.

Off-grid solar is the epitome of energy resourcefulness. It is truly going out on your own, without the safety line of the local municipal power supply. By becoming off-grid, you're committing to only using the energy that you generate through your own hard work and the tools at your disposal.

What is off-grid solar?

Off-grid solar requires completely cutting the cord, so to speak. With no electrical grid tying you into the system, you're really on your own. This has a number of benefits. For one, you never have to pay an electrical bill again! You also never have to worry about losing power due to the electrical company, whether from a storm bringing down power lines or an increased load preventing the electrical company from meeting demand.

However, there are obvious downsides as well. You've only got the energy you can generate yourself, and if you run out of it then you're out of luck. Plus, off-grid systems are more expensive due to the need to provide 100% of your power and store it in expensive battery systems. But for many, the disadvantages pale in comparison to the freedom of being on your own. Or you just live too far from town to have an electrical hookup. Either way, let's get off-gridding!

Necessary components

We briefly discussed the components used in off-grid solar systems in the subject's overview in Chapter 3. Also, many of the parts used in off-grid solar installations are the same as those used in grid-tie systems that we covered in the previous chapter. I won't simply repeat the descriptions of those components as it'd be a waste of perfectly good paper, so make sure you read about solar panels and inverters in Chapter 8 on grid-tie systems. For now, we'll cover the rest of the parts that you'll need for an off-grid system.

Junction and combiner boxes

Your off-grid setup will likely have multiple solar panels connected in series strings and potentially in parallel arrays as well. These connections will need to be made in junction boxes so that the connections are protected from the elements and accessible for maintenance. A typical junction box is a waterproof plastic box. It may be mounted on the solar panel itself, on the roof, or on a wall. Many solar panels will come with pre-installed junction boxes on the back of the solar panel.

Charge controller

After your solar panels generate power, you'll need a way to send that power to your batteries in a useful form. This is where a charge controller comes into play. The two main types of charge controllers were discussed in Chapter 8, but just to summarize, the choices are PWM and MPPT charge controllers.

For a small 12 V system and even for some 24 V systems, a PWM charge controller might be a good choice. They are cheaper and simpler, but not as efficient. On the other hand, MPPT charge controllers allow you to work with higher DC voltages on the solar panel side of the circuit to increase efficiency and reduce the cost of the wiring needed to transfer power with low voltage but high current DC electricity. If your solar panels are more than 40-50 feet from your charge controller, an MPPT charge controller will likely pay for itself in the savings in copper wire alone. MPPT charge controllers are also more efficient, so on a large enough system they can often pay for themselves over time with their extra energy generation.

Batteries

After your charge controller, you'll need batteries. We discussed batteries in detail in Chapter 4, but to summarize in case you skipped that chapter, your choices are mainly limited to lead acid and lithium-ion batteries. Lead acid batteries are cheaper but don't last as long, while lithium-ion batteries can cost 2-4x as much but last 5x longer or more, often making them cheaper in the long run. A large factor in the decision is often how much money you want to invest up front.

If you'll be building an off-grid solar power setup, be sure to go back and thoroughly read Chapter 4 on batteries.

Inverter

The inverter in an off-grid system is likely to be fairly large, as it will have to power the entire home. In Chapter 7 on planning for a solar powered home, we discussed ways to reduce your energy consumption and thus reduce the size of the inverter needed for such a system. Even so, powering all of your devices is going to require significant power for most people, unless you lead a very low-electricity lifestyle.

For off-grid inverters, it is important to choose an appropriate inverter to meet your needs. Simple AC-DC inverters, sometimes known as square-wave inverters, are much cheaper than sine-wave inverters. They can be used for many basic electronics, but don't work as well with sophisticated or delicate electronics like computers and televisions. For these, you need a sine-wave inverter.

If you're just powering some lights, a small fridge and some battery chargers in an off-grid cabin, you might be able to get away with a cheaper inverter. For anyone powering a standard home with everyday use devices, a sine-wave inverter is a necessity. It provides cleaner AC electricity that will make all of your devices simply work better.

We also talked about determining the appropriate power level for your inverter in Chapter 7. It is important to factor in the power required by all of your devices that will be running simultaneously as well as the startup power required by some of those devices. The surge rating on your inverter will help you determine if it can handle the extra startup power needed by many powerful devices.

There are also some inverters on the market that include a built-in charge controller. These are more expensive and usually meant for larger systems, but they can reduce complexity and make the installation process simpler and easier. If you have the extra money and a large enough system, one of these hybrid charge controllers and inverter combinations might be right for you.

Fuses and disconnect switches

Fuses and disconnect switches are important parts of any solar power installation, and especially in an off-grid system that concentrates all of your energy in a single location. Fuses protect vital components of the system from operating at power levels that are outside of their ratings and at which damage may occur. Fuses can be used for short circuit protection, such as when placed on a battery to prevent a short circuit from destroying a battery, or for overcurrent protection, such as when placed between the battery and the inverter to protect the battery from providing too much current and overheating. Circuit breakers can be used as well, and are preferable in many cases since they are resettable and don't need to be thrown out and replaced like a blown fuse.

Disconnect switches are important safety components as well, but perform a separate function. They allow you to disconnect or isolate components in the circuit. This electrically removes them from the circuit without requiring you to physically disconnect any wires or move any components. This can be helpful during maintenance or during emergencies when you want to quickly remove a component from the circuit.

Meters

Meters indicate how much energy you are producing and consuming, and are useful for many purposes. They can help you determine how efficiently your system is operating by comparing how much energy you generate from your solar panels versus how much usable energy you consume from your inverter. They can also provide you with insight as to how different devices and loads in your house affect your energy consumption. Meters can be a great tool both for optimizing your system and for satisfying your curiosity about the performance of your system at any given time. Some meters require you to visit the meter and inspect it manually, while others can wirelessly transmit their data to a central readout, computer or phone application for remote and long term analysis.

<u>Gas/diesel generator and battery charger</u>

While not strictly necessary, a gas or diesel generator can be an important piece of backup equipment for an off-grid solar power system. Ideally your system will be designed to be large enough to handle a few days without the sun. However, no off-grid solar power system can operate forever without the sun. During long storms or other extended periods without sufficient sunlight, your batteries may run empty (or below 50% for lead acid batteries, which should be considered as empty to extend battery life for any case short of an emergency).

In this scenario, a gas or diesel generator can be used to quickly recharge your batteries and operate your AC devices until the sun returns.

Design and setup

Just like for a grid-tied solar power system, the solar panel installation for an off-grid home will follow the methods detailed in Chapter 7, where we also covered the design of the series and parallel layout of the panels and the wiring size selection. Remember, this is where online wire calculators can come in very handy. Whether you're using rooftop or ground level solar panels, the basic installation process is all the same. A sturdy frame and well grounded panels are essential, just like we covered in Chapter 7.

Now let's focus on the electrical side of things. You'll need to start by connecting your solar panels into series strings and parallel arrays. The more panels you place in series in a string, the higher the voltage. This higher voltage means that your current is lower for the same amount of power, allowing you to use thinner wires. However, you must ensure that your voltage isn't higher than the maximum input voltage of your charge controller. Many off-grid systems use a nominal 48 VDC system, which usually entails four 18 V solar panels connected in a series string. This can result in a DC voltage as high as 80 V under maximum conditions, so always double check that your charge controller can handle this. Some charge controllers are limited to 60 V, in which case you'd want to stick with just three 18 V solar panels in a series string.

If you have more than one string, you'll need to connect the strings into parallel to form an array. More strings in an array will result in more current and thus more power, but won't increase the final voltage.

These connections between solar panels should be waterproof and housed in a junction box, usually hidden behind the panels themselves. They should be easily accessible in case you ever need to perform maintenance or remove a panel. The junction box may also contain fuses to protect the solar panels in the event of a short circuit or reverse current flow.

From the junction box, or from the last junction box if you have multiple, a minimal number of wires will exit towards your charge controller. Smaller systems may only have two DC wires exiting to charging controller, while larger systems may need to run multiple sets of wires to handle the power loads. Before the wires carrying DC power from your solar panels will enter your charge controller though, you'll need to include a DC cutoff switch. This will cut power to your charge controller and can be used either during maintenance or in the event of an emergency.

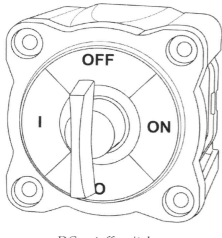

DC cutoff switch

Your charge controller will be mounted close to your batteries, so your wires from the solar panels may have to travel a long distance to reach the charge controller. If possible, it is best to minimize this distance in order to cut down on power loss over long wire runs. The best way to reduce this distance is to locate your batteries as close to the solar panels as possible. If they are on the roof of your house, then this likely won't be an issue. Roof mounted solar panels can send their wiring straight through the roof and into the house. However, if your solar panels are mounted elsewhere on your property, you might want to build a battery shed for them to be closer to the panels. Some people prefer to house their batteries in a separate shed anyways to keep them out of the house. This can be for safety reasons or simply to free up space in the house or basement.

For charge controllers, remember that your two options are PWM charge controllers or MPPT charge controllers. For an off-grid home, you will almost certainly be working with an MPPT charge controller. An off-grid home or cabin requires a relatively large amount of power, and to effectively transfer that power without spending a fortune on gigantic copper wires, you'll be using higher voltage DC power from multiple solar panels wired in series. Low 12V DC power can be easily handled by a PWM charge controller, but for higher voltage and to maintain higher efficiency, you'll want to use a good MPPT charge controller.

Your charge controller's output will be connected to your batteries in order to charge them, but you'll want to include a DC cut-off switch here as well. Again, this switch can be used during maintenance of the batteries to ensure that current is not flowing to them, and can also be used during an emergency if a problem occurs with the battery requiring a quick disconnect from the charger.

Most off-grid charge controllers are fairly advanced and will allow you to program in the exact specifications of your battery. Using different voltage levels, you can control to what extent your batteries are charged by the charge controller. Lead acid batteries should be charged completely, while lithium-ion batteries may be charged completely or partially. In fact, charging lithium batteries to only 90% instead of 100% capacity can actually help improve their useful lifespan considerably. Some studies have found that 90% charging can even double the life of lithium-ion batteries.

Next you'll connect your batteries to your inverter, but with a fuse in between to prevent your inverter from pulling more current than the amount for which your batteries are rated. Be sure to choose your fuse appropriately as the correct size fuse will vary from one system to another based on the batteries you are using. If your batteries can output 300 A, then you'll need a fuse that will blow to protect your batteries from being drained at over 300 A. I like to use Marine Rated Battery Fuses (MRBFs) as high quality, powerful fuses.

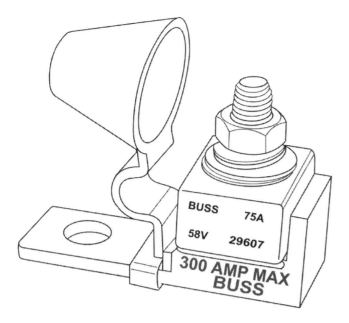

Marine Rated Battery Fuse (MRBF)

You will also want to include another DC disconnect switch between your battery bank and your inverter. Again, this can be used both during maintenance and in the case of an emergency. Activating this switch will cut off all power draw from your batteries, meaning they will not be providing any current to the circuit downstream on the inverter side. However, if your DC disconnect switch to the charge controller remains in the connected position, you could still get a shock when working upstream on the charge controller side of the circuit. Remember to disconnect the appropriate switches when performing maintenance on your system.

Your inverter will draw power from your battery bank directly. In some cases, your charge controller might also have a "load" output option, usually outputting 12 VDC. This is generally meant for low power devices and not for your large inverter, as that amount of power can often burn out your charge controller. Rather, the batteries should act like a buffer and perform the brunt of the work in supplying power to the inverter. Some charge controllers are designed to connect to both the batteries and the inverter. In this case, the charge controller can provide some of the power demanded by the inverter directly. This would be an alternative to sending that current first through the batteries, which can result in somewhat lower efficiency as the batteries don't charge at 100% efficiency. Some current is always lost as heat during battery charging. Not all charge controllers have this option. If yours doesn't, use the simple method of connecting the charge controller to the batteries and then the batteries to the inverter.

If you would like to include an amp hour or watt hour meter in your system, this is the place to include it. If your meter has an external shunt, you'll wire the shunt between the batteries and the inverter. If the meter has an internal shunt, you'll wire the entire meter between the batteries and the inverter. This will allow you to measure how much energy in watt hours your system has provided to your home over its operating life (or since the last time you reset the meter). Some meters can also measure instantaneous power, peak power and other interesting data, and even transmit that information wirelessly to a computer or phone application.

Depending on the size of your off-grid system, you will either plug your AC devices directly into your inverter or your inverter will feed into an AC breaker box to distribute the AC power to different circuits in your home.

A small hunting cabin can usually get away with plugging a minimal number of devices into the outlets on an inverter or into a multi-outlet extension cord plugged into the inverter. Larger off-grid systems, such as those powering an entire off-grid home, will likely have multiple circuits for different rooms in the home. In this case, your inverter will need to be wired into your AC breaker box to connect to these circuits. In many areas, this job must be performed by a licensed electrician. In some areas, the work can be done yourself but must be certified by a licensed electrician first. You should check your local laws to determine what codes apply in your area.

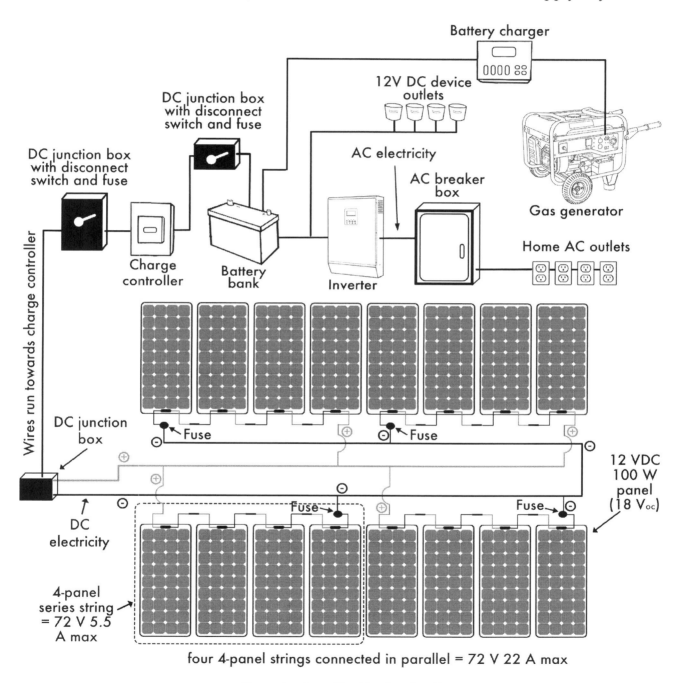

Example of an off-grid solar circuit

Lastly, you'll likely want to include a hook-up in your system for a generator. If your batteries are ever depleted, a gas or diesel generator can recharge them and keep you supplied with electricity. It's not the quietest or the cleanest solution, but it can keep your fridge and everything else running in a pinch.

You'll want a fairly powerful battery charger so that you can charge your batteries quickly without having to run the generator all day. Be sure to not exceed the maximum charging power for your batteries though. Your battery charger will be connected in place of your charge controller, or you can wire in an extra charging port on your battery so that you don't need to disconnect your charge controller.

You may also want to create an input for your generator in your AC breaker box as well, especially if your generator is capable of providing more power than your batteries can consume during charging. This extra AC power can be used to power devices in your home at the same time that it is charging your batteries. If you go this route, you'll likely want to install an inverter bypass switch between your inverter and your AC breaker box to ensure that power is only flowing from the generator into the breaker box and not back into the inverter.

Some larger off-grid systems include a generator with a sensor that can detect when the batteries are low and will automatically kick-in to charge the batteries as necessary. For a large off-grid home installation, this can be a nice feature that saves you extra work. However, it is an added complexity that might not be necessary for smaller systems. It also requires that your generator always be in a ready-to-operate configuration and location, which may or may not be possible for your specific scenario. If your system is properly sized, generator usage should be rare. In such cases, wheeling out the generator isn't much extra work.

Chapter 10: Solar powered vehicles and boats

Vehicles and boats can be prime candidates for solar power. They often spend a large portion of their time outside, have large flat surfaces on their roofs and require significant energy for tasks like accessory devices and locomotion. However, there are some unique issues that are related to solar power systems installed in moving objects. In this chapter, we'll discuss what you need to know to add solar power to your vehicle or vessel.

Solar panels and components in motion

Any device that will be mounted on a moving surface must be designed to handle the forces and vibrations that it will be expected to incur. On a car or RV, this will usually be bumps on the road and wind gust loads. On a boat, this could be high intensity vibration from an outboard motor. Other moving projects have additional unique parameters. Regardless of the scenario, you'll have to plan for the motion that will be experienced in your project.

This motion will have the largest effect on your decisions for the wiring and solar panels. Stranded wiring should *always* be used for devices that will be in motion or experience vibration. It has somewhat lower current carrying capacity as compared to solid wire, but the individual strands withstand vibration and motion much better and won't fatigue and crack as quickly as solid wire. Keep in mind that improperly thin or low strand count wire can still fatigue and crack under intense vibration though, so when in doubt, use heavier gauge or higher strand count wire.

For solar panels, you may want to consider flexible panels instead of rigid glass framed panels. Not only will rigid glass frame panels be more vulnerable to damage from vibration and shock, but they are limited to flat surfaces. Unless you're working on the flat roof of a large RV or van, flexible solar panels can be much easier to install on the somewhat rounded surfaces found on many vehicles. They also withstand vibration and shock loading much better than glass panels.

However, since we mentioned RVs, this is one of the few cases where glass panels may be just as suitable. The large flat surface of an RV can easily accept strong mounts to support large glass panels. Also, shock absorbing material can be built into such mounts to help dampen vibration. Many commercially available RV solar panel mounts are available for this specific purpose. In general, I still prefer to use flexible solar panels on most vehicle applications for the reasons mentioned above.

Next, consideration should be taken in designing your system based on the power needed for the load. If you are powering accessories in a vehicle or boat, your load will likely be relatively small. If you are powering a drive train, your load will be much larger. Let's start with planning for powering accessories, and then we'll cover the additional requirements of powering a drivetrain.

Supplemental solar power for accessories

In order to design a solar power system to provide power for vehicle accessories, you'll need to perform an energy audit to determine exactly how much power and energy you'll need.

<u>Energy requirements</u>

For example, if you are building a small vehicle like a bicycle, tricycle or velomobile and want to power devices such as lights, a horn, speakers, etc., then you can simply add up the power requirements of each device and the amount of time you'll be powering them.

For example, you might have the following accessories with the following power requirements:

LED lights: 5 watts
Electric horn: 35 watts
Speakers: 20 watts

Total: 60 watts

This total of 60 watts means 60 W of instantaneous power. If you wanted to run these devices directly from a solar panel, you could probably get away with a 100 W panel, which would be more likely to create 60-75 W in good conditions. Realistically though, most of the time you will probably use only the 5 W lights and 20 W speakers, with only occasional horn usage. That means you could really be using a max of 25 continuous watts of power, and an occasional peak of 60 W.

By adding a battery into the mix and creating a system that stores power, the battery can act as a buffer providing the power source and allowing you to use a smaller solar panel. It also gives you the added benefit of being able to use your lights at night, which is probably pretty important. In general, you'll likely want to include a battery in your vehicle solar power system unless you only plan to use the solar power in your vehicle during the day and during periods when the sun isn't obscured by clouds.

Next, you'll also need to know the total energy use. We'll keep this simple and assume you want enough battery to last for one day (or you can just multiply these answers by however many days of backup power you need). You'll need to calculate the amount of time you'll use the accessories each day. Let's imagine that these are the figures we come up with:

LED lights: 2 hours
Electric horn: 15 seconds
Speakers: 2 hours

We can determine the total energy usage in watt hours by multiplying the watts required by each device by the hours in use. That gives us:

LED lights: 5 watts x 2 hours = 10 watt hours
Electric horn: 35 watts x 0.0042 hours = 0.1458 watt hours
Speakers: 20 watts x 2 hours = 40 watt hours

Total: 50.1458 watt hours

As you can see, the horn accounts for a tiny fraction of our total energy use, so we are essentially at 50 watt hours of energy needed each day. In this case, as long as our battery can provide 50 watt hours of energy and 60 watts of peak power for the times we use all three accessories simultaneously, we can use a much smaller solar panel to charge our battery than originally calculated to power our devices directly. A 20 W solar panel would give a realistic 14-15 W of power in full sun, so 3-4 hours of sun would be enough to nearly completely charge our 50 watt hour battery. If we are optimistic that we can get a good 6-8 hours of sun per day, we could likely get away with a smaller 10 W panel. As you can see, by using a battery as the primary power source instead of the solar panel, we are able to reduce the size of the solar panel from 100 W down to just 10 or 20 W.

This energy audit was fairly simple because we only had a few devices and could easily check their power levels, resulting in simple calculations. However, if you have a large project such as an RV solar power installation, it will be more of a challenge to add up the power and energy requirements for all of your accessories. In this case, a better method might be to track your energy usage over a period of time. By installing a watt meter on your battery between the output of your battery and the input of your fuse box, you can measure the energy being used by all of the accessories in your vehicle. You'll want to perform this test over a period of time that you'll be using the vehicle under normal conditions so that you get an accurate indication of total energy usage. Many watt meters can also measure peak power use, which will be helpful in determining the maximum amount of power you used when operating multiple devices at once.

Battery selection

When choosing your battery, you'll have the same options as listed in Chapter 4 on batteries, mainly lithium-ion versus lead acid batteries. However, for mobile applications, lithium-ion batteries are often a better choice due to their lower weight and ability to discharge fully (thus not requiring twice the weight and volume of batteries, as would be necessary with lead acid batteries, to match the same energy capacity of lithium-ion batteries).

Therefore, when considering a solar power project for most small vehicles and vessels, lithium-ion batteries are usually the better option. For larger projects, like in an RV or large boat, the weight and space advantages of lithium-ion batteries are less important. In these cases, you're back to comparing the relative advantages and disadvantages of both types. Review Chapter 4 on batteries to refresh your memory on that information.

You'll also need to decide on the proper voltage for your application. Most mobile applications for vehicles will require a 12 VDC system, as most vehicle accessories operate on 12 VDC. For large systems such as those on RVs and on some large boats, a 24 VDC system may be common, but this is usually limited to very large vehicles and vessels.

Next, you'll need to calculate the correct capacity of your battery. As we demonstrated above for our velomobile, an energy audit determined that we needed approximately 50 Wh of energy. If we have a 12 V battery, then we can calculate the required Ah size of the battery simply by dividing the 50 Wh by 12 V to give us 4.17 Ah. Ideally we will somewhat oversize the battery. In this case, a 12 V 5 Ah battery will give us approximately 20% more energy than we need.

Other necessary components

In addition to the solar panel and battery, you'll need a few other components to build your solar power system. A charge controller will be necessary to charge the batteries. For a 12 V system of low to medium power, a PWM charge controller will be a cheaper, though somewhat less efficient option. If you are using higher voltage or want increased efficiency, an MPPT charge controller will be necessary, though be warned that they cost more than PWM charge controllers.

An AC inverter might be necessary if you want to power AC accessories from your DC battery. This will be more relevant to an RV system than to a smaller project like a velomobile or electric canoe.

You'll also need some assorted switches and fuses to protect your components. Lastly, you'll need stranded wire of sufficient gauge and electrical connectors to wire everything together.

When it comes to choosing your wiring, use an online calculator to determine the correct wire gauge for the power level and length of wire you're using. My favorite is the Renogy wire gauge calculator but there are many wire calculators available online for free. Generally, for short runs of wire in systems carrying less than 30-40 A, I use 12 AWG stranded silicone wire. However, you'll want to confirm the correct gauge wire for your system based on its unique requirements.

Connecting everything together

To create your solar power system to power vehicle accessories, you will install your components using the following setup. Start with your solar panels. If you're using a 12 V system, you'll likely be using either a single panel or multiple panels connected in parallel to form an array. You should not connect multiple 12 V panels in series for a 12 V system, unless you are using an MPPT charge controller to handle higher DC voltage, or unless you have lower voltage panels such as 6 V panels.

However, many mobile systems for low power uses will only require one panel anyways, so you won't have to worry about making parallel connections between panels. If you are using multiple panels in parallel, you'll simply connect the positive wire of the panels together into one wire, and the negative leads of the wires together into another single wire. If using three or more panels in parallel, you should add an appropriate fuse rated for just slightly higher than the maximum current output of a single panel.

Next your panel or panels will connect to your charge controller at the panel input location. Your battery will then connect to the battery output location of your charge controller. Your charge controller might have a third connection location marked "load". If so, you can connect your accessories to this location if they match the voltage output and don't pull more power than the charger is rated for. For example, 12 VDC accessories would be fine for a 12 V charge controller's load port, but 24 VDC or 110 VAC devices should not be connected to the load port on that charge controller because the 12 VDC output will not be sufficient to power those devices.

You can also connect your accessories directly to the battery, though it may be preferable to include an inline fuse, especially for higher power devices. This will prevent them from pulling more current than the battery can safely supply, which could occur if the devices ever malfunctioned or fell overboard on a watercraft. You may also want to include switches inline between the battery and accessories as well. This can be useful for accessories such as lights that you might want to enable and disable without unplugging them from the battery.

If you are using an inverter, such as for an RV system, you'll connect it directly to your battery. Ensure that the inverter is rated to provide more power than you'll be drawing from it at any one time. If you are only powering simple electronics, such as chargers, speakers, or other small electronics, you can likely get away with a simple, cheap inverter. These are usually square-wave inverters. If you'll be powering more sophisticated electronics such as computers, monitors and televisions, you'll likely need a more expensive sine-wave controller. These produce "cleaner" electricity with less noise and will help your electronics function more optimally.

Solar power for electric vehicle drivetrains

Solar power can also be used to power the drivetrain of an electric vehicle or vessel, such as an electric tricycle, surrey cycle, go-kart or boat. Just like when powering accessories in a vehicle, the solar power can either be used to directly power the electric motor in the vehicle, or it can be used to charge a battery that powers the electric motor.

Unless the power required to drive the vehicle is very small or the surface area for solar panels is very large, it will be difficult to generate enough solar energy to directly power the drivetrains on most electric vehicles. In most cases, a battery powered electric vehicle with simultaneous solar powered charging is a much better option.

Solar powered direct drive

If you want to forego a battery altogether, then you'll want to maximize the solar panel surface of the vehicle and minimize the energy required. The surface area of your vehicle is likely limited, but more effort can be made on reducing the energy requirement. Reducing the speed of the vehicle is the best way to reduce energy required, as the energy necessary to power the vehicle increases exponentially as the speed of the vehicle increases. Reducing the weight of the vehicle also reduces the amount of energy demanded, as does reducing the aerodynamic or hydrodynamic drag.

Once you have reduced the power necessary to the lowest level manageable, you're ready to start preparing your system. Your solar panels will need to provide as much power as your motor will require. For a 250 W motor, you'll need more than 250 W of solar panels, as your solar panels will be lucky to produce 70% of their rated power in full sun. Thus, for a 250 W motor, you'll likely need at least 350 W of solar panels to reach your motor's full power potential.

Also keep in mind that the exact power needed might not be decided by your motor, but rather your motor controller. For example, a motor rated at 250 W might be connected to a 24 VDC motor controller with a current limit of 15 A. This would result in a peak current draw of 24 V * 15 A = 360 peak watts. This is the actual power you'll need to plan for, not the 250 W motor power rating.

Next, consider that you might want to place a voltage regulating device in between your solar panels and the motor. This can help smooth out the voltage being supplied to your motor and controller, as the voltage and current from your solar panel will vary as sun and load conditions change.

As you can see, the method of attempting to directly power the drivetrain of an electric vehicle or vessel using only solar panels and no battery storage is rarely a good method. Not only does it make it hard to fit a sufficient number of solar panels on the vehicle to meet the motor requirements (the 250 W motor in our example is a paltry ⅓ horsepower, too small for most scenarios) but it also means the vehicle can only work then the sun is shining and not obscured by clouds, trees, buildings, etc. A much better method would be to use a battery to power the drivetrain and solar panels to charge the battery.

Battery powered electric vehicle with solar charging

Not only is a battery powered electric vehicle superior in power and performance to a direct solar powered drivetrain, but it also allows you to start the day on a full charge by charging the battery from the grid overnight.

This setup will also be easier to implement to an existing battery powered electric vehicle, as you are essentially building a simple solar charger to add to the vehicle.

Whether you're working on a solar powered car, bicycle, go-kart or boat, the basic steps for planning and installing the solar powered charging system are the same.

First, determine the amount of charging power you desire. It is unlikely that you'll be able to charge the battery at the same rate that it is being consumed (otherwise you could remove the battery altogether and use a direct drive system). This means that you'll be extending the range of the electric vehicle with solar charging, but not giving it infinite range.

An electric surrey bike could easily fit 3 solar panels on its roof

For example, let's look at an electric surrey, which is basically a four wheeled bicycle. If it has two 500 W motors in the rear wheels and uses 1,000 W of power, it would be difficult to provide all of that power from solar panels. However, we might be able to fit three 100 W solar panels on the roof of the surrey. Assuming our 300 W of solar panels can generate 200-250 W of real world power, we can charge at close to 25% of the consumption of the battery (which is 1,000 W). By reducing the power requirement of the vehicle somewhat, such as reducing the speed of the vehicle, we might be able to reduce our consumption down to 500 W. At that level, we could be charging the battery nearly half as fast as we are draining it. If you factor in frequent stops, we might be getting even better than a 50% rate of return.

You'll have to determine the amount of charging power you want for your project in order to calculate how quickly you'll be replenishing your battery. As solar panels become more efficient and more power dense, it will be easier to charge at higher rates, and the goal of creating nearly infinite (daytime) range by charging at the rate of consumption will become easier and more attainable without huge surface area requirements.

But for now, let's stop dreaming about the future and stick to working in the present. Installing such a system is actually fairly simple, believe it or not. I'm assuming you already have your electric vehicle built, or at least have the plan. That means you already have a motor, a motor controller, and a battery. Now we have to design and install the solar charger.

The main component of the charger will be the charge controller. This will interface between the solar panels and the battery. If you are using a 12 V system, standard PWM charge controllers can work well for you. Most electric vehicles will use a higher voltage system though. In this case, either an MPPT charge controller or a DC-DC converter with a CC-CV (constant current - constant voltage) charging scheme for lithium-ion batteries can be appropriate. I like using DC-DC converters because in essence, that is what an MPPT charge controller is, but bare board DC-DC converters are often cheaper because they are not specifically designed for the solar industry, meaning they do not come with an extra high price tag.

For lithium-ion batteries, it is important that your DC-DC converter or MPPT charge controller is in fact a CC-CV device. This will ensure that once your battery is fully charged, it cuts off power and doesn't trickle charge like a lead acid battery charger.

You'll need to program your charge controller or DC-DC converter to the proper full voltage for your battery. Most lithium-ion batteries charge at 4.2 V per cell, meaning that you'll multiply 4.2 V by the number of cells in series to determine the proper charger voltage. For example, a 48 V lithium-ion battery with 13 cells in series will require a 54.6 V charging voltage. As discussed in Chapter 4 on batteries though, you might want to undercharge your lithium-ion battery slightly to increase cycle life.

The output of your charge controller or DC-DC converter will connect directly to the charging input on your battery. For a lead acid battery, that's probably the main battery terminals. For a lithium-ion battery, you'll likely find at least one of the two charging leads originating from the BMS, though this might not be obvious if the battery is entirely sealed from the factory. Just make sure to check with your vendor regarding which is the proper charging port on a lithium-ion battery, if you aren't already certain.

The input to your charge controller or DC-DC converter will come from your solar panel(s). If you have more than one solar panel, they can be connected either in series or parallel, depending on if you are attempting to increase the voltage or current. Generally, higher voltage and lower current is desired so that you can use thinner wires to transfer the DC current.

It is a good idea to include a fuse and cutoff switch between the solar panel(s) and charge controller or DC-DC converter, as well as between the charge controller or DC-DC converter and the battery. These extra protections can help protect your expensive components in the event of a malfunction, and the cutoff switches can allow you to make adjustments or perform maintenance without current flowing through the system.

Solar power for electric boats

Electric boats can be an incredibly fun project to build and use, as they allow you to access some beautiful, scenic areas without the effort of paddling and without the noise of a gas engine. By adding solar power charging to the system, you can easily extend the range of the vessel and take advantage of the plentiful sun. Plus, you can even use the panel as shade on smaller boats like canoes and kayaks that don't typically come with awnings. Elevating the solar panel creates a nice little canopy and shade, and also prevents the panel from taking up valuable space inside the boat.

Parts selection

The best hull to start with for your first simple electric boat is a canoe or kayak. This allows you to start small and reduces the overall power demand. Small skiffs and fishing boats can also be good candidates, but the more water you displace and the more hull surface you put in the water, the more power you'll need, increasing the power demand and cost of the system.

After you've chosen your hull, you'll need a motor. There are purpose-built electric boat motors out there already, and many come with kits to adapt them to a canoe or kayak. These are great solutions, but they can be quite expensive. We're talking more-than-$1,000 expensive.

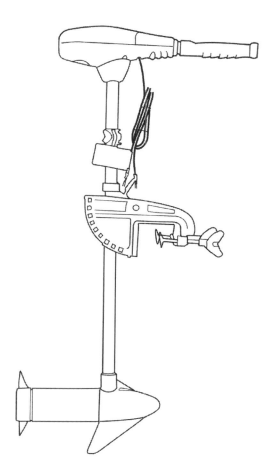

For a solution that works just as well but is orders of magnitude cheaper, I like to use electric trolling motors designed for larger motor boats. They are almost always 12 V motors and are usually found in the ½-1 hp range. They are meant for use as a bow thruster on larger boats for positioning, or to troll along at a snail's pace. However, when installed on a much smaller boat like a kayak, these trolling motors can power you to much higher speeds. They usually cost a few hundred dollars new, but they are also commonly available in used condition for less than $100. Check sites like eBay or Craigslist for good deals in your area. The main downside to using a trolling motor is that you'll have to build some custom method to mount it to your specific hull. Don't worry though, if you weren't a DIYer then you wouldn't be reading this book.

From this point, you'll need a battery to power the motor. Many people use a car battery. This will work, but it isn't a great option as car batteries are designed for sudden bursts of high power and very short discharges. This application is going to be long periods of medium power and deep discharges. 12 V deep cycle marine batteries are better, but still quite heavy and bulky. If you can afford it, a 12 V lithium-ion battery will not only be lighter, but it will last many more years and cycles. They are also much smaller, meaning you don't have to fill half of your boat with lead acid batteries to achieve a full day of motoring around the bay up and down the river.

Your battery will simply connect to the input on your motor, though you'll probably want to add a fuse in between the two to protect your battery from overcurrent. The throttle on your motor is probably located on the tiller, allowing you to steer and control the throttle with a single hand.

Here's where the solar power comes in. We can greatly extend the range and runtime of our electric vessel by charging the battery while we're using it. With a canoe or kayak, most of the surface of the vessel is unused. A simple frame can be rigged on top of the hull to support multiple solar panels. The more solar panels you can fit, the faster you can charge your battery.

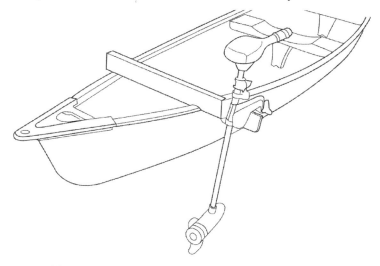

Using 2x4 beam to employ transom-mount motor

Because you will almost certainly be working with a 12 V system to match your 12 V motor, it will be easiest to use 12 V nominal (18 V open circuit) solar panels. If you have only one panel, you do not need to make any inter-panel connections. If you have multiple panels, you'll want to connect them in parallel to form an array. This will increase the current produced by the solar panels but the voltage will remain the same at approximately 18 V.

As we discussed, more solar panels will give you more power in the form of higher current, but you must ensure that the current is not higher than the maximum rated charging current of your battery. Lead acid batteries will likely have a printed maximum charging rate, but lithium-ion batteries might not be as clear. For lithium-ion batteries, the maximum charging rate often depends on the BMS, if one is included in the battery. Be sure to inquire with the vendor of your battery if you are unsure of the maximum rated charging current of the battery.

Making the connections

You'll start by connecting your solar panels in parallel (if using more than one panel). Next, you'll connect the solar panel output to the input of a charge controller. A 12 VDC PWM charge controller should be fine for this system. If you need maximum efficiency, an MPPT charge controller will be slightly better, but costs significantly more. The slight increase in efficiency is rarely worth it for a pleasure craft of these low power levels.

However, you do need to ensure that your solar panel power level is appropriate for the charge controller. For example, a 100 W 18 V solar panel would produce approximately 5.5 A max current. A charge controller rated for 12 VDC and 10 A would be fine for this level, but three of these panels in parallel could burn out that charge controller because they could potentially generate 16.5 A of max current. In that case, a 20 A or 30 A charge controller would be safer, giving you more room under the max limit of the charge controller.

Lastly, you'll connect the output of the charge controller to the charging input of the battery. This will allow you to charge your battery at the same time as it is being discharged through the discharge leads to the motor. The amount of charge it receives as a proportion of the discharge rate depends on both the power of your motor and the power of your solar panel array. By adjusting the power levels of the two, you can dial in the right specifications for your requirements.

Additionally, adding a meter can be beneficial so you don't run out of battery power when you're least expecting it. I can imagine that the irony of literally being up a creek without a paddle wouldn't be nearly as funny in the moment.

A simple way to measure the charge level of a 12 V battery is by reading the voltage. Both lead acid and lithium-ion batteries will start with a higher voltage when fully charged and drop to a lower voltage as they discharge. However, this voltage drop occurs at a different rate for the two different chemistries of batteries. That means you need to get a meter that converts voltage to battery percentage that is specific to either a lithium-ion or a lead acid battery. There are many different cheap meters available for these types of applications. Simply search for "LED battery capacity voltage meter" on your favorite ecommerce site such as eBay, Amazon or AliExpress and you'll surely find many different examples.

A better way to measure battery capacity is with a watt meter that tracks amp hour use. This is more exact and can tell you exactly how much energy you've used from your battery, down to the decimal.

A simple voltmeter-based meter, like the one described above, can be wired in parallel to your battery, meaning the red wire connects to the battery's positive wire and the black wire connects to the battery's negative wire. A true wattmeter, like the type described above after the voltmeters, must be wired inline in series, meaning the battery plugs into the "source" side of the meter and the motor plugs into the "load" side of the meter. The advantage of a watt meter is that it can also indicate your instantaneous power usage, allowing you to adjust your power up and down to learn how it affects battery consumption. If you're running low on battery, this extra data can help you conserve battery more effectively as well.

Waterproofing

One big caveat for a solar powered electric boat is waterproofing. Anything electrical around water needs to be given extra care. If you're in a saltwater environment, you'll need to be doing an even better job of waterproofing than for a freshwater environment, as the saltwater is even more corrosive. Solar panels often come with waterproof connectors such as MC-4 connectors, but it is still best to keep these covered and out of the way of splashing water. You want to avoid any water reaching the connectors or the charge controller, since the charge controller is usually open to allow for cooling air to pass through it. If you can find a potted charge controller, meaning all the components are covered in epoxy to protect against the elements, that would be even better!

For a lithium-ion battery, I usually like to place it in a dry bag and roll the edge with the wires extending through the roll. This keeps any water from getting into the battery or connectors. Lead acid batteries are often too big for this, so you might want to keep them in a large plastic tub. Keep in mind though that lead acid batteries can off-gas overtime, so it is best not to seal them completely.

Chapter 11: Passive solar projects

When most people think of solar power, they think of photovoltaic cells and solar panels that convert the sun's rays into electricity. That is one way to harness the energy of the sun, but it is definitely not the only option. In fact, it is often even easier to capture the sun's energy and use it for heating instead of generating electricity directly via photovoltaics.

This is known as passive solar power, where the sun's energy is captured in the form of heat energy. In this chapter, we'll cover a number of uses for this passive solar power and the ways you can create your own passive solar projects.

Solar cookers

Solar cookers are one of the simplest forms of passive solar energy use. While most people in the Western world are familiar with cooking on gas or electric stoves, many people in developing countries rely on the power of the sun for cooking. In these areas, solar cookers help reduce deforestation by cooking food without the need for cutting down trees for firewood and improve health by reducing the amount of smoke inhaled during the cooking process.

But you don't need to travel to the end of the Earth to learn to cook with the power of the sun. You can perform the same process in your own backyard!

There are two main styles of solar cookers that are commonly used around the world: open solar concentrators and closed solar ovens. They both operate using similar principles by reflecting the sun into a smaller area, but they have different advantages and disadvantages.

Open solar concentrators use some type of curved dish or panel to reflect the sun's rays into a central point. A common method is to use a large dish shaped collector on an articulating frame. The dish can either be purpose made for this application or recycled from something else, like an old satellite dish covered in reflective material. A pot or kettle is placed at the focal point of the dish, supported by a rack above the dish. The sunlight that strikes the dish is concentrated towards a central point, heating the pot or kettle to cook the food inside or boil the water. As the sun moves across the sky, the rack can be turned to remain aimed towards the sun. A simple pin or nail pointing in the same direction as the dish can be used to aim the solar collector. When the rack is moved until the pin or nail head creates no shadow, it is pointed directly at the sun.

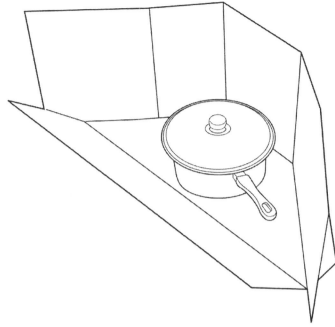

While dish concentrators are most efficient, even simple concentrators made from flat objects can create powerful solar cookers. A cardboard box cut open and covered with aluminum foil or mylar film can be arranged around a pot to reflect sunlight onto it. This won't work as quickly as a dish shaped concentrator, but it can still cook a meal if given sufficient sunlight.

A solar oven combines the concept of a solar collector to concentrate the sun along with an enclosed box with a clear roof to take advantage of the greenhouse effect, where air warms up inside of a closed system but the heat can not easily escape.

A simple solar oven is just a box with reflective walls inside and a glass or clear

Flat reflective panels concentrate sunlight onto pot

plastic cover on top. Food is placed in the center of the box, usually in a cooking vessel, and the top of the box is closed. As sunlight enters through the clear top of the box, it reflects off the shiny walls of the interior of the oven, eventually striking the food in the center of the box. The heat can not easily escape and more sunlight entering through the clear top, further increasing the temperature of the box, cooking the food.

A simple upgrade to this type of solar oven is to include a parabolic trough in the bottom and a rack to elevate the food. This trough will better reflect and concentrate the sunlight towards the center of the box where the food is located.

To increase the amount of solar energy entering the box, flaps can be added to the top of the box on hinges. The angle of the flaps can be adjusted up and down to direct more sunlight into the top of the box, further increasing the heat of the oven and speeding up the cooking time.

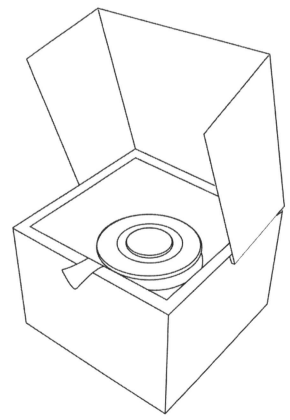

Clear lid box adds greenhouse effect

Residential hot water heater

Passive solar power also works great for heating water for home use. It is a shame to pay for gas or electricity to heat water when your roof is constantly being pummeled by heat energy from the sun! In many parts of the world, especially areas with abundant sunlight like the Middle East, passive solar water heaters are the most common form of home water heaters.

These passive solar water heaters, known as thermosiphons, are incredibly simple as they do not require any type of pump or external electrical source to operate. They work completely independently and automatically!

A thermosiphon hot water heater requires two main parts: a passive solar collector and a storage tank. The collector panel is composed of a shallow box with a clear glass top. Inside are a series of copper pipes that run from the bottom to the top of the shallow panel. The panel is placed on an angle so the top end is elevated higher than the bottom. The inlet to the copper pipe inside the panel is located at the bottom of the panel, while the outlet of the copper pipe is located at the top of the panel. The outlet from the top of the panel is connected by pipes to the top of the storage tank, while the bottom of the storage tank is connected to the inlet at the bottom of the panel.

In order for the thermosiphon to function properly, the storage tank needs to be elevated higher than the panel. The tank is normally placed on an elevated platform of approximately 3 feet or 1 meter, and the panel is usually placed at an angle below the tank.

The tank is filled with water, which fills the copper pipe inside the panel as well. Water is circulated through the panel without a pump due to the thermosiphoning effect. The effect works like this: when sunlight strikes the dark panel, it heats up the copper pipes in the panel, thus heating the water inside the pipes. As the water heats up, it becomes less dense and rises up the copper pipes inside the panel. Upon reaching the top of the panel, the water exits the panel and flows into the top of the storage tank. This upward motion of the water in the panel's pipes causes a suction action, creating a syphon that pulls water from the bottom of the storage tank into the bottom of the panel. As long as the water in the storage tank is cooler than the water in the solar collector panel, the flow will continue. Once the water has been circulating in the system long enough and the water in the storage tank reaches the same temperature as the solar collector panel, the water no longer automatically rises through the panel and the flow stops.

If hot water from the tank is used in the home, water from the local water main is pumped in to replace it. Suddenly the water in the tank is at a lower temperature than the solar collector panel, which causes the thermosiphon action to restart until enough water flows through the system to reach equilibrium again, shutting off the thermosiphon action.

At night, the solar collector panel cools off, meaning that it is cooler than the warm mass of water in the storage tank. This prevents the warm water from flowing through the system into the cooler solar collector panel because the thermosiphon only works when the water in the solar collector panel is warmer than the storage tank. When the sun comes back out in the morning, the flow restarts and the heating continues.

With a sufficiently large water storage tank, many areas of the world have no need for an electric or gas water heater. Even in the winter, the sun can be sufficiently strong to heat the dark solar collector panel and create enough hot water for home use. In areas with very cold winters or long periods without sun, a supplemental electric or gas water heater might be necessary. This can be added to the system in parallel, only kicking in when the water in the passive solar water heater tank is not sufficiently hot.

Pool heater

Another great use for solar water heating is for swimming pools. Electric or gas pool heaters require incredibly large amounts of energy to heat large volumes of water. But the sun already provides large amounts of energy for free, so why not take advantage of it?

Unlike with a thermosiphon hot water heater, it is difficult to make a purely solar powered pool heater because the storage tank (the pool) usually can't be placed at a higher elevation than the solar collector panel, as the pool is normally built into the ground. For this reason, a small electric pump is usually necessary to keep water flowing through the solar collector panel. However, the amount of electricity used by the pump is only a tiny fraction of that used by conventional electric pool heaters, so we are still saving a significant amount of electricity by using this method.

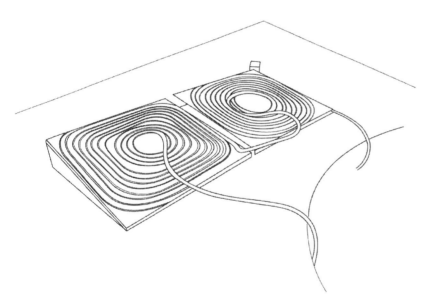

Just add a pump and you've got a DIY solar pool heater

A simple solar collector panel can be created by taking a black hose and coiling it around itself in an expanding circle. This can be laid on the ground next to the pool, or built into a black box with a clear top to make it more efficient by heating faster with the greenhouse effect. The hose will need an inlet and outlet that both reach to the pool, but ideally are spaced out somewhat to prevent hot water from the inlet from immediately entering the inlet and traveling back through the system.

Even with strong sun, it will likely take many days to significantly increase the temperature of the pool, so make sure you begin heating the pool earlier than the day before your big party. This is not a fast method, but it is nearly free when you consider that almost all of the energy is provided by the sun. You can even run the pump from a solar panel to have an entirely solar powered pool heater!

Camping shower

The solar pool heater in the previous example takes a long time to heat up because of the large amount of water, but a small volume of water can heat up very quickly in the sun. If you've ever left your water bottle in the sun for just a few minutes and come back to a warm bottle of plastic-flavored tea, then you'll know exactly what I'm talking about.

This effect can be used to create a very efficient camp shower. When camping for more than a day or two in a row, a shower can be a nice treat - or necessity for some people! But a cold sponge bath is less than enticing to most people. A solar powered camp shower is an easy project that will make you a hero during your next hiking or camping trip.

The shower itself is simple to make. Basically, you take a dark bag or bottle, place it in the sun, then wait for it to heat up. Depending on the size of the container, you'll likely have hot water in a matter of a few hours. If you set up the equipment at lunch time, you'll likely have a hot shower waiting for you by dinner.

For a single person shower, a gallon of water is plenty for a camping scenario. For a small amount of water, a dark trash bag (heavy duty, not the economy kind) can be sufficient. Fill it with water, hang it from a tree branch and let it heat up in the sun. When you're ready for a shower, poke it with a sharp stick in a couple of places and let the good times roll.

For a more eco-friendly and reusable option, consider a rigid plastic container. A 2-liter bottle such as a soda bottle can be painted black to heat up quickly in the sun. Drilling a few small holes in the lid can create an effective shower head. Tie some rope around the bottle near the bottom, or tape it if the bottle is too smooth to get good grip with the rope, and hang it upside down for a shower. Making a few of these bottles at once means multiple people can take showers, and also helps regulate water use so one person can't use up all of the hot water.

To go even bigger, look for a jerry can, fuel can (clean, of course!) or an old cooking oil bottle from restaurants. I have a 20-liter plastic vegetable oil bottle that I got from the dumpster behind a restaurant. It works great! The hard plastic

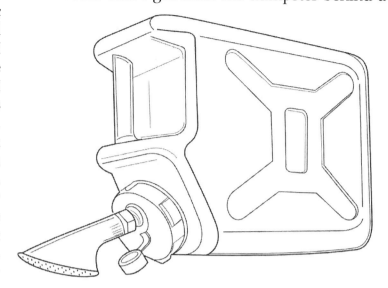

is sturdy and it has a wide screw top. I had planned to paint the plastic black but I found that even leaving it dark yellow, the water heated up in about three hours, so I didn't even have to paint it. All I did was drill a few dozen 1 mm holes in the cap. Now I let it sit in the sun to heat up for a few hours and then throw a rope over a tree branch to hoist it up in the air. Hanging upside down, the water sprinkles from the many 1 mm holes in the cap and creates a perfect hot shower that is sufficient for a few people. In the future, I plan to make a small upgrade for it by attaching a shower head to the cap for a more spread out shower stream.

Residential heating

Solar energy is great for heating water, but it can also be useful for heating air too. Using a solar air heater can save you plenty of money on your heating bill every year, making it worth considering!

Solar air heaters use the greenhouse effect, the same effect we've talked about already that causes a car to heat up like crazy when parked in the sun. When all of that sunshine enters the windows of the car, the heat energy passes through with it. However, most of the heat energy is passed into the material in the car and very little gets reflected back out.

This principle is quite annoying for cars, but can be used to our advantage for solar air heaters for the home. A great DIY project is a window mounted solar air heater. This can fit any window that slides up to open, which are common on many homes. You can also make it work with other styles of windows, though you might need to add a bit more custom work in order to seal the area around the heater to prevent cold air from leaking in.

The collector is a simple frame shaped like a box and placed at an angle, leading up from the ground to the window. This can be built out of plywood, and lining the inside with a sheet of styrofoam insulation is a good idea to make the collector more efficient.

The inside of the collector should be painted black to absorb solar energy in the form of heat. In addition, a heat absorber from a thermally conductive material such as a metal panel is placed inside the box. Aluminum is a good choice since it won't corrode if it gets wet and has high thermal absorption, but steel can also work if you're on a budget. Make sure the metal is also painted black to aid in heat absorption. Another good option for solar heat absorber material is to use tubes created from steel food cans painted black. These black cans will heat up, and the tubes created by placing the cans end to end will funnel the warm air up the panel.

Lastly, cover the top of the collector with a clear material, such as glass or polycarbonate. Polycarbonate is lighter and also not fragile like glass, though it can cloud over time. Corrugated polycarbonate is best, as it uses the lowest amount of material but is still quite strong and rigid due to the corrugations.

To keep the entire panel airtight, use silicone caulking on all of the joints. Not only will this help your solar air heater operate more efficiently, but it will also keep rainwater and dew out of it, extending the useful life of the heater.

Your frame should be built so that the bottom is open and rests near the ground, while the top faces the open window. The window will be closed around the top portion of the collector, and you can use foam or insulation panels to fill in any gaps around the collector and the window frame.

The collector itself should be angled towards the sun as close to 90 degrees to its highest point as possible. This will ensure that the most solar energy possible enters the collector.

When sunlight strikes the collector, it passes through the clear top and hits the black heat absorber inside. The temperature of the heat absorber increases, heating the air around it. The air rises as the temperature increases, traveling through the collector and window opening into your home. Behind it, air is pulled through the collector by the warm air rising. This new air heats up as it passes over the thermal absorber, in turn rising and continuing the cycle of pulling more air inside the heater.

A similar concept can be used to create a roof mounted solar air heater. A passive solar collector box is built using the same concept, with a clear top and a black heat absorber inside. However, two holes are cut inside the bottom of the box. It is mounted on your roof and ducting is used to circulate the air from the passive solar collector to vents in the house.

The outlet vent, or air supply, should be mounted higher on the wall, while the inlet vent, or air return, should be mounted lower on the wall. A fan is used to circulate air through the ducts. The air passes through the solar collector where it is heated by the thermal absorber before flowing back into the home.

A thermostat should be connected to the fan to control the power and timing of the air flow. This system works great during the day, but you don't want the fan running at night or when the sun isn't shining since it would cool the air in the dark solar collector, having the undesirable effect of cooling your home instead of heating it!

A few of these solar collectors used in your home can drastically reduce the need for electrical or gas powered heat, saving a significant amount of energy and money in the process.

Chapter 12: Examples of solar power projects

Talking about solar power projects in general, as we have done throughout most of this book, is an important part of learning the theory and steps involved in such projects. However, it can be even more helpful to see this information applied in practice using real examples. In this chapter, I am going to walk you through how I would go about applying what we've learned in this book to actual solar powered projects, from the design and parts selection stage to the actual implementation and construction. Even if these projects do not match the exact specifications required in your build, they will hopefully serve as a useful guide that can be altered to fit your specific needs.

Grid-tie family home

Grid-tie homes are a great way to get started in solar power for the home. You can start with a system sized to fit your budget and needs, then expand as necessary when your resources and requirements change.

In this case, I'm going to plan a grid-tie system for a medium sized family home. The goal of this system will be to create most of my electricity that I need during the day. If I suddenly need more electricity than my solar panels are generating, I'll simply draw that extra power from the grid. And if I'm generating more electricity than my home is using, I'll sell that extra electricity back to the power company via net metering. And since this is a grid-tied system and I won't have any batteries, I'll be using electricity from the grid at night or anytime the sun isn't shining, such as during cloudy periods.

I'll start by determining my solar panel requirements. By checking my energy bill, I see that my home uses around 750 kWh of energy per month, or around 25 Kwh of energy per day. That's a significant amount of energy. Generating all of that energy with solar panels is possible, but many people don't have enough roof space. For my goals, I'll start with something a bit more manageable.

Let's say I have enough space on the portion of my roof facing the sun for 10 panels each rated for 235 W. That's a total of 2,350 W of power from the solar panels under ideal conditions, or more realistically around 1,700 W of power if we are assuming that I'll get around 70-75% of the rated power out of the panels in good conditions.

After talking with solar panel installers and experts in my area and using some online sun calculators, I've learned that based on my area, I can expect the 10 panels to generate around 15 kWh of energy on good days in the summer and around 7 or 8 kWh of energy in the winter, where the days are shorter and the sun is less direct.

That means that in the summer I'll be generating more than half of my daily energy needs in the period of about 8 or 9 hours of sun, likely giving me a surplus and the ability to sell that extra energy back to the power company. In the winter I might not be producing as much energy as I use during the day, depending on how many devices I'm using in my home at once. In that case I'll need to supplement the solar panel energy with grid electricity occasionally. But that's ok - that's why I'm building a grid-tie system - so I have the grid to fall back on when I need it.

I buy a kit of 10 solar panels as well as the mounting racks and hardware to install them. I make a day out of it, invite some buddies over and get to work on the roof. We drill holes for the aluminum racks, filling the holes with silicone caulk and using either neoprene washer screws (for drilling into roof rafters) or toggle bolts (when we can not drill straight into the rafters). We mount the solar panels on the racks and ground the entire system using proper heavy gauge solid copper grounding wire running down to a copper grounding rod hammered into the ground.

For this setup, I'm going to use a microinverter system. This will give me the highest efficiency for my grid-tied setup by allowing each panel to generate electricity at its maximum power, even if one panel is partially shaded or obscured. The microinverter string is connected to each solar panel at the rear of the panel. At the final panel, the wires connected to the microinverter string are fed through a series of conduit pipes to the edge of my roof and then down the outside of my house to the electrical panel on the side of my house.

To ensure that this part is done correctly and safely, I'll pay a licensed electrician to perform the step of integrating the output of my solar panel string into my electrical panel. I'll also need to have the power company come out, verify the work, then swap out my old meter for a two-way net meter. This net meter will allow me to sell the extra power back to the electrical company during times when my panels are generating a surplus.

Lastly, my microinverter system comes with a gateway module that plugs into my router and uploads my solar panel energy generation data to the internet so that I can monitor all of the data in real time on my computer or phone. It communicates wirelessly with my meter on my electrical panel to track the instantaneous energy generation of my entire system. Using the data, I can see graphics indicating how much power each panel is generating at any one time, how my energy generation changes over the course of a day and as the seasons change, and I can track how much energy I've consumed myself or sold back to the electrical company, among many other interesting features.

Unlike with off-grid systems that include more components such as charge controllers and batteries, after installing my solar panels, microinverters and panel/meter connections, I'm finished! Now I can just sit back, relax and watch my solar panels generate power in the tracking software. In the future I can always expand my system if I want to generate more energy. By simply adding more solar panels and microinverters, I can increase the amount of energy I produce each day and ensure that I have a surplus of energy to sell back to the grid.

Off-grid hunting/vacation cabin

Ah yes, the good old-fashioned off-grid cabin. Great for weekend getaways, hunting trips or summer camping. The same setup here could also be used for other structures such as separate garages, workshops or sheds that need power for additional lighting or other electrical appliances.

In this example, let's imagine we have a cozy little one room cabin that is far away from any electrical source and thus must be rigged for off-grid solar electricity.

The cabin is currently lit just by sunlight streaming in through the windows during the day and by kerosene lamps at night. To upgrade this, we'll add some energy efficient LED light strips. One 5 meter (16 foot) strip of LEDs consumes 60 W of energy and should be plenty to light up my single room cabin.

While we're adding electricity though, we should probably plan for the capability to power more than just lights. Being able to charge devices like a laptop, cell phone or radio would be nice, so let's plan for that as well.

To determine the amount of energy and power my system needs, I'll perform an energy audit. My planned devices' power requirements and the estimated daily usage are:

LED light strips: 60 W and 6 hours of use per day = 360 Wh per day
Laptop charger: 40 W and 2 hours of use per day = 80 Wh per day
Cell phone charger (x2): 10 W each and 3 hours of use per day each = 60 Wh per day

This means that I could theoretically be using a maximum of 120 W at any one instant if all devices are being used simultaneously. I'll also have a total daily energy usage of 500 Wh per day.

At 500 Wh per day, I'll need at least a 500 Wh lithium-ion battery or at least a 1,000 Wh lead acid battery (to avoid draining the lead acid battery past 50% depth-of-discharge). In this case, I'll use a lithium battery because the cabin is small and I don't want to take up too much space with big lead acid batteries. Also, because this is a small system, the battery won't be very large and thus the price difference between lead acid and lithium is not as large either.

I'll be using a 12 V system since this is a small setup and I don't need to run the wires from the solar panel very far. For a 12 V battery with 500 Wh of energy, I'll need a battery with at least 42 Ah (calculated by 500 Wh ÷ 12 V = 41.67 Ah). However, I'll probably want some extra capacity just in case, so let's double it and go with approximately 80 Ah.

For my area, I don't want to rely on getting more than six hours of sun per day. There might be more, but a conservative estimate is always safer. If I want to be able to charge a 1,000 Wh battery with only six hours of sun, I'll need to charge at a rate of at least 167 watts (calculated by 1,000 Wh ÷ 6 hours = 167 watts). If I use two 100 W panels, that "200 watts" of power will be closer to 140 real world watts. This would be close to what I need, but just to be safe, I'll go with three 100 W panels. I'll mount these on my cabin's south facing roof (since I'm in the Northern hemisphere) and properly ground them with 6 AWG grounding wire connected to a copper grounding rod hammered into the ground outside.

I'll connect these three panels in parallel to create a solar panel array. Since each 100 W panel provides approximately 5.5 A max (in perfect conditions), I'll need a charge controller that can handle at least 16.5 A. There are many cheap 12 V PWM charge controllers in the 30-40A range, so I'll use one of those.

My solar panels are connected in parallel in a junction box behind one of the panels with a 7A fuse on each panel. Then the single set of wires extends down through a rubber boot flashing in my roof and into my cabin. Using conduit to run the wires down the wall to an electrical cabinet (a glorified plastic box on the wall), I connect the wires first to a DC disconnect switch and then into my charge controller's solar panel input. The battery output on the charger controller is then used to connect the battery's charge connector to the charge controller, but with a DC disconnect switch in between the two.

I set my charge controller to a final voltage of 12.6 V, which is the proper full voltage of my 3s li-ion 12 V battery, which is actually an 11.1 V nominal battery that charges fully to 12.6 V.

Next I will add a 30-amp fuse to the positive wire on the discharge port of my battery, since it is rated for 30-amp maximum discharge. I'll never need close to that much power (which would be approximately 350 watts) since my max instantaneous power needs are only 120 W, but it's good to have it there to protect the battery just in case someone was to plug in a more powerful device like a toaster or microwave.

After the fuse, I'll connect the output of the battery to the input of my inverter. My inverter has a minimum voltage input of 10 V DC. My battery can actually discharge to 9 V DC, meaning that I won't be using the bottom-most portion of my battery's capacity. This is ok though, since I chose a battery that had twice as much capacity as I needed. In fact, its even healthier for my battery not to discharge it all the way.

I can plug my AC devices like my laptop charger or phone chargers into the inverter, which will create the 110 VAC that my devices require.

I'll also connect the 12 V LED strip to the output of the battery after the fuse as well, but with a switch inline to turn the lights on and off. This LED light strip doesn't need AC electricity like my laptop or phone chargers do. Instead, it needs 12 VDC, so it can run directly from the battery.

And that's it! Now I have a 12 V solar powered off-grid system. The three 100 W panels on the roof should easily charge my battery to full capacity each day, and I have more than enough capacity for my daily needs, which will be useful if I have a day without much sun.

If I wanted to run bigger appliances such as a refrigerator or stove, I'd follow the same steps but use more solar panels, a more powerful charge controller and inverter, and a larger battery to store and deliver that extra power.

Solar power charging backpack

This is a fun project for me because I love the outdoors and enjoy going on multi-day hiking trips. However, I unfortunately have a hard time "cutting the cord" and going without connection to the outside world. I like to have my phone on me, not just for emergencies, but also so that I can check-in with loved ones at night and still keep tabs on what is going on in the world.

For a one or two-day trip, my phone battery will usually last. But if I'm going on a longer trip or I have a lot of people in my group that also want to charge off of a single backup battery, it's hard to make it last long enough. That's why a solar powered charger on a backpack is a great piece of gear to have, and a fun project to build yourself. Sure, you can buy a folding USB solar charger on Amazon for $50-60, but where's the fun in that? Let's build one ourselves and save money at the same time.

The first thing we'll need is to determine our power level. At minimum, a USB charger needs to be supplied with approximately 5-6 V and 0.5 A, but that would make for a pretty slow charger. Increasing the current will increase our charge time. Bumping up to 1 or 2 A should be enough for a decently fast charge. We could increase to 2 A for an even faster charge, but we want this to easily fit on the outside of a backpack for hiking, so let's keep it a bit lower to reduce the overall size of the panels we need.

If we want 5-6 V on the load side of our solar panel, we'll need closer to 9 V of open circuit voltage. That would require 18 cells in a panel. While I could make my own panel from multiple PV cells, the parts in this project are already so small and cheap that it is almost not worth the time and effort. Heading on over to my favorite Chinese shopping site, AliExpress, I find that I can get a 3 W, 330 mA, 9 V panel for just $6 with free shipping to the US. Each panel measures 6" x 8" (125 mm x 195 mm) and they are epoxy encapsulated, making them more rugged and protected. If I had four of those in parallel, I'd be up to 12 watts and 1.33 A of output. Works for me!

I'll also need my charging module. Also on AliExpress, I've found a nice little dual USB port charging module that works with solar panels. Total cost with shipping: $3.80. It also has the ability to connect to a battery pack as well, so you could include a battery with your setup if you wanted. If we choose to include a battery, my solar panels will charge the battery while I am hiking and then I can charge my phone from the battery at night even when the sun is hidden. That's a nice option to have, so I'll consider it. But let's start with the solar part first.

I want this contraption to be fairly small for packing down, and open up to hang from my backpack, so I'll join the solar panels in a way that allows them to fold together.

A great way to do this would be to glue two pieces of nylon webbing to the back of each panel. That way they can be wrapped around each other for storing and the nylon webbing will create a small cushion between each panel to keep them from scratching or cracking each other. You could also use some clear packing tape if you wanted to do a quicker and cheaper solution, but the nylon straps will be more durable.

Next I need to wire these four panels in parallel, since they are each already 9 V. By wiring them in parallel, their voltage will remain the same but their current will be added. That means I'll increase the total current to 1.33 A (from 0.33 A x 4 panels). I'll use stranded wire because the device will be moving around, and stranded wire holds up much better to movement and vibrations. Since we're using less than 1.5 A of current here, the wire doesn't have to be very thick. Some high strand count 20 AWG silicone wire is just fine. I'll solder a length of red wire to each of the four (+) positive pads on the backs of the solar panels as well as a length of black wire to each of the four (-) negative pads on the backs of the solar panels. I'll also be careful to leave enough slack between each panel so that the force of pulling stays on the nylon webbing and not the wires I've soldered to the panels.

Next, I'll solder the end of the two wires to the solar panel pads on my charging board, which are indicated by the T+ and T- markings on this particular board. At this point, I should have a fully functional solar USB charger. Testing it by plugging in a phone into the USB charging port and placing the solar panels in the sun shows that it's working! And the total cost was just under $30, including the little bit of wire and nylon webbing, though many people have scraps of those laying around and could build this project for even less money. Not bad - we built a charger for half the price of a commercial one on Amazon!

But we can make our charger even better than an Amazon charger. Remember the optional battery port on our charging board? Let's add a battery to it so we can charge our devices at night too. Most phones have a single cell li-ion battery (3.6 v) in the range of 1.5-3 Ah. This is around the same capacity range as most 18650 li-ion batteries. I can add a couple 18650 cells to my setup and be able to completely charge two phones, or halfway charge four phones. Man, my friends are going to love me!

The best and safest way to connect 18650 cells is to spot weld them. However, most people don't have a spot welder at home. That leaves two other methods: no-weld 18650 battery building kits or soldering. The kits are recommended since soldering can damage the cells. However, I'm going to just look the other way and solder two 18650 cells in parallel by joining their positive ends together on one side and their negative ends together on the other side using either a piece of nickel strip or copper wire. Again, I don't recommend soldering directly to these cells, but so many people do it anyways that I will mention that it is possible.

Now that I've got a 2p battery module (two cells wired in parallel), I can connect the positive terminal to the battery (+) positive pad on the charging board and the negative terminal to the battery (-) negative pad on the charging board. When my solar panels are exposed to sunlight, they'll charge my phone if it is plugged in, or they'll charge the built in battery if there's no phone to charge.

Ideally I'll stash the electronics and batteries in a small project enclosure or pill box with some silicone to seal it against the elements.

The last thing to do is simply tie my charger to the top of my hiking bag using the nylon webbing straps and let it hang over the top and back of my bag. As I move around during the day, the panels will experience different levels of sun exposure. Surely there will be times that I'm hiking towards the sun, at which point they won't generate much power on my back, but as the sun moves and I move with it, the panels are sure to get some sun throughout the day, and all that energy will be put to good use charging my devices. And to make the charger more effective, I can point my backpack towards the sun anytime I sit down to take a load off and rest.

Solar powered canoe

Canoeing, kayaking, stand up paddle boarding and other self propelled watercraft are fun ways to get around on the water in a small, nimble vessel. If you're a fisherman, they can be some of the only ways to get into the best shallow water or narrow passage fishing spots. However, they all share one major problem: they are self propelled! Exercise is great, but sometimes it would be nice to just sit back, relax and let the boat paddle itself.

Converting your self-propelled watercraft into an electric boat is a great way to save your energy and still get around on the water without having the annoying scream of an engine in your ear or the smell of gasoline and exhaust in the air. By adding a solar charger into the mix, you'll increase your range and make sure you aren't stuck up a creek without a paddle… or without a charge!

Since this book is really about the solar portion, I'll just give a quick overview of the motor and battery part. There are a number of fancy little waterproof electric props out there that cost thousands of dollars, but one of the best ways to convert your canoe or kayak to electric drive is with an outboard trolling motor meant for larger pleasure craft. On a 16-foot V hull speedboat, an electric bow thruster is really only meant for steering and maneuvering, but on your little boat it can propel you quite well for hours on end. Look for used electric outboards on auction sites like eBay to find a steal, often for well under $100. Or you can buy one new, usually in the price range of $150-250 for 12 V models.

In my case, I'll pick up a 40 lb thrust 12 V model, which should be plenty for me. I'll have to rig something to hook it up to the back of my canoe, but hey, that's what DIY is all about!

A lot of people make the mistake of trying to run these motors from a car battery. That's a great way to give a car battery an early demise. Deep cycle marine batteries last longer but are quite heavy. If you can swing it, go for a lithium-ion battery. A 4s li-ion battery is actually around 14.4 V, so your 12 V motor will spin a bit faster, giving you more speed.

In my case, I'm going to build my own 4s 60 Ah lithium-ion battery. If you want to go this route, I highly recommend reading my book *DIY Lithium Batteries: How To Build Your Own Battery Packs*. I simply can't explain all the intricacies of battery building in a single section here.

The motor will connect straight to the battery, though an inline fuse would be a good idea to protect the battery against overcurrent or short circuits. Depending on the current draw (try measuring it with a clamp-style DC amp meter), a fuse in the range of 40-60 A is probably sufficient. Bring a few with you though in case you blow one while you're out on the water!

In my case, I can test the maximum current draw of my motor by putting the prop in water and giving it max throttle while using one of those clamp-style DC amp meters to measure the current in one of the battery wires. I find that the maximum current draw it is pulling at its highest power setting is 26 A, so I'll add a 40 A fuse. This is high enough over the normal current draw that it won't blow during normal use, but if there is a short circuit and the current shoots up above the normal level, the fuse should blow and protect my battery.

Now let's get to the solar. We're going to need some solar panels and a charge controller to make this system complete. An electric trolling motor pulls a lot of power, usually in the range of 300-750 W. Unless you can fit that much power in solar panels on your boat (doubtful, unless you've got a limousine of a canoe) then you'll be charging at a lower rate than you're using. That's fine, it just means you can't use the system indefinitely, as you'll eventually run out of battery. However, the solar panels will certainly increase your range before the battery runs dry.

Let's say I can fit three 18 V 100 W solar panels onto my canoe up front, sitting sideways across the canoe. Each is about 39" x 21" (100 cm x 55 cm), so they'll take up a good amount of room, but they should fit. They'll need to be strapped down nice and tight though so they don't roll off the edges.

I'll connect the three 18 V panels in parallel, which will keep their voltages the same, increasing their current from around 5 A each to 15 A total for the system.

Now I'll need a charge controller that can handle 300 W of power. I can choose between PWM and MPPT charge controllers, but since I'm staying at 12 V, PWM charge controllers will likely be cheaper. A common size is 30 or 40 A, which is well over my needs, so that sounds good. I'll definitely be staying under the rated limit of 30 or 40 A. This way I'm not stressing the components too much by pushing them to their limits.

In a small boat, the wire lengths will be pretty short, so I can get away with thicker wire without breaking the bank. The wire that comes already installed on the panels will be sufficient for making the parallel connections and connecting the three panels to the input of the charge controller. The battery output from the charge controller will be carrying a maximum of 15 A of power, though likely closer to 10 A under real world conditions. For 10 A, 12 AWG wire is more than sufficient for our needs.

From here, the solar system is complete and ready to go. As long as the batteries and panels are connected to the charge controller, and as long as there is sun out, the batteries will be charging. Depending on how much I use the motor, I can probably add about 50% more range to my day using this method. If I'm stopping often, such as for fishing, I could probably get away with both a smaller battery and fewer or smaller solar panels, as I'd be recharging during breaks where I use no motor power. Depending on your needs though, you may want to increase or decrease the solar array and battery size accordingly.

Solar powered electric bicycle charger

If you know anything about me or my other writings, you'll know I'm a big advocate of electric bicycles. They are clean, efficient and fun alternatives to cars and other forms of transportation. They use only a tiny fraction of the energy of larger vehicles, even energy efficient ones, and are often better choices for getting around cities that are prone to traffic and congestion.

However, if you don't keep your battery charged, you'll end up pedaling more than you expected. A solar powered charger is a great addition to an ebike and allows you to further reduce your carbon footprint by ensuring that the electricity used in your ebike comes from a renewable source.

A 100 W solar panel might be hard to mount on a bike

Ebike solar chargers are usually quite big though, so don't expect this to be something that you can stash in your pocket and take with you. To be effective, the smallest possible ebike charger is probably going to be around 100 watts. A 100 watt panel is approximately 3 feet or 1 meter long - definitely not pocket sized. So unless you have a bicycle trailer, this is type of charger is better kept stationary at your home or office, or wherever else you charge. You could build this project with a 50 watt solar panel, but it could take more than a day's worth of sun to get a full charge at that rate.

To begin this project, we'll need a few simple parts: A solar panel, a charge controller, some electrical connectors and a few short lengths of wire.

The solar panel's wattage will decide how quickly you can charge your ebike. The higher the wattage, the faster the charge. A good place to start for a slow but reasonable charge is 100 W. If a 100 W panel can reasonably output 75 W of charging power, and an ebike battery is around 500 watt hours (such as a 48 V and 10 Ah battery), then charging should take around 7 hours, which is about a full day of usable sun. Using two 100 W solar panels can halve that charging time. For me, I'll start with two panels. 200 W is a pretty common level for electric bicycle battery chargers. If I want faster charging in the future, I can add another panel or two in parallel.

Searching around, I find that 18 V, 100 W flexible solar panels can be purchased online from China for around $100 a piece. These panels will be good if I want to move them around or take them in a trailer on my ebike, since they can allow a bit of bending due to their semi-flexible nature. If I just want to leave them stationary and prop them up on the roof of my garage or hang them out the window of my office, that will be fine too. They come with grommets in the corners, which should make mounting even easier. The grommets also allow me to connect the two panels to each other with string and fold them in the center like a notebook. Oh, the possibilities!

Ok, so now I've got my panels. Next I'll need a charge controller. There are lithium-ion specific charge controllers available in the $40-50 range that come in a nice enclosed case and are meant to easily mount on the wall with pre-made mounting holes. However, I can save some money by getting a barebones, exposed board DC-DC boost converter capable of charging lithium-ion batteries. This means that the converter should operate with a CC-CV (constant current - constant voltage) mode, where the voltage increases and the current remains constant until reaching the set voltage, at which point the current is lowered while the voltage stays constant, and then cuts off current altogether when the current reaches a low level. This is necessary for lithium-ion battery charging. A 900 W DC-DC boost converter with digital display and controls is available from AliExpress for $17.

One note about these types of devices: even though the converter is rated for 900 W, I would never actually try to run 900 W through a device like this. Never trust the peak anything ratings of cheap Chinese electronics. I'm definitely comfortable pushing 200 W through this device, but 900 W seems like more than this thing should be able to handle. The peak specs on these types of devices are almost always exaggerated, so when choosing cheap components like these, always buy one rated for higher power than you need.

Now for the connections. I can actually connect my solar panels in either parallel or series, since my DC-DC boost converter (acting as my charge controller) has an input range of 8-60 VDC. To make this more efficient, I'll wire them in series to get higher voltage. With the DC-DC boost converter's maximum input voltage of 60 VDC, the two panels in series are well within the specs at just 36-40 VDC. I could even add one more panel in series in the future and stay just under the 60 V limit.

The two panels will then be connected to the positive and negative input port on the DC-DC boost converter. On the other side of the board, I'll connect a short length of wire, around 3 feet or 1 meter, to the positive and negative output ports. On the end of the wire I will add a connector that matches the charging port on my battery.

With a bit of sun on the panels, the DC-DC converter should start right up. I'll use the buttons on the digital display to dial in the correct voltage for my battery, which is equal to 4.2 V multiplied by the number of cells in series for a lithium-ion battery, or 3.7 V multiplied by the number of cells in series for a LiFePO$_4$ battery. Since my battery is a 14 cell, 52 V li-ion battery, my full charge voltage is 58.8 V. Most common 48 V li-ion batteries are 13 cells and require 54.6 V, while 36 V li-ion batteries are 10 cells and require 42.0 V for charging. If you aren't sure how many cells are in series in your battery, double check with your manufacturer or measure the output voltage on the charger that was supplied with your battery.

Now I can solar charge my ebike battery anytime there is sun! Plus, since my DC-DC converter is adjustable, I can dial in the exact charging voltage to an even lower amount if I want to slightly undercharge my lithium-ion battery and extend the cycle life of the battery!

Solar powered oven

A solar powered oven is a fun project to make because it is so incredibly simple. For this project, I'm going to make a simple, collapsible oven that can be folded down and taken anywhere.

To keep things cheap, I'll start with a cardboard box. The exact size of the box is not critical, but the larger the box is, the more food you can fit inside and the more solar energy it will capture.

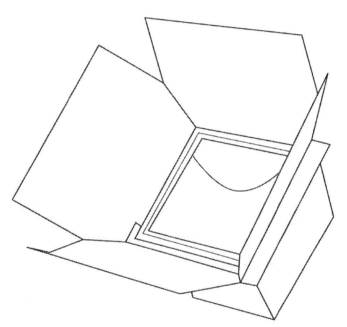

I'll open the box and measure the dimensions of the four inside walls. Then I'll cut pieces of reflective mylar foil to the size of each wall and spray the inside walls with adhesive spray. After the walls are coated with adhesive, I'll lay a piece of mylar foil on each wall, being careful to lay them flat and avoid bubbles or creases. I'll then place mylar foil on the inside of the four box flaps at the top of the box too.

Next, I'll find another piece of cardboard or poster board that can bend into a smooth arc. This will be the parabolic solar collector. I'll cut a piece of mylar foil and glue it to the collector just like I did to the interior walls of the box and the box flaps.

The collector will be placed inside the box so that it forms a trough. Ideally, you should aim to create a complete half circle if possible. This will direct the sunlight at the center of the box.

Next I'll place a few small holes in the side of the box. I can either place four holes to support the four edges of an oven rack, or two holes for a rotisserie rod. A rotisserie rod is great for cooking things that need to turn and cook evenly, like hot dogs. The rotisserie rod can slowly rotate the food so it is evenly cooked by the reflected solar rays. A rack is better though if you want to cook in a pan or pot.

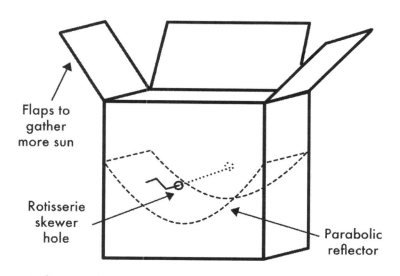

Flaps to gather more sun

Rotisserie skewer hole

Parabolic reflector

Lastly, I'll place a clear cover over the top of the box. This can be as simple as piece of cling wrap for sealing food, or a sheet of polycarbonate or glass to make it more durable.

Now when I want to start cooking, I'll place my food either on a rotisserie stick or on an oven rack above the parabolic solar collector. I'll place the clear top back on the top of the box to trap in the heat, and I'll angle the flaps on the top of the box so that they are reflecting more sunlight down through the clear top. All that's left to do now is wait for my food to heat up and I'll be ready to eat the first solar-cooked meal from my new solar oven!

Solar powered deck/garden lights

This is great project that can be expanded or altered in many ways. If you have an outdoor space to which you'd like to add lights but don't want to run long extension cords, a solar powered and battery connected light setup can be a great option.

In this example, let's say I've got a seating area on my property, such as in the corner of my back yard) that is far enough from my house that I don't want to run a long extension cord to it above ground or lay the cord on the ground as a trip hazard. Plus, running an extension cord out there each time will just be a pain. If this for a daily use location, like garden lights or motion powered security lights, you definitely don't want to be running around with an extension cord every night. A better solution is to run the lights from a battery that is solar charged, creating a small off-grid system.

In this case, my sitting area needs some flood lights. A few 5 W LED floodlights will be just fine, and I can put them on a post or hang them in trees around the sitting area. LED light strips or rope lights could be another option for more romantic lighting, but I'll leave that up to you. For my case, three 5 W floodlights will require 15 W of power.

If I want to use them each night for 4 hours, I'll need 60 watt hours of power, calculated by 15 watts x 4 hours of use. That means I'll need at least 60 watt hours of battery capacity, and any extra will be good for days that were cloudy where I didn't get to generate as much energy that day.

I think I'll go with a lead acid battery in this case, since it does not need to be lightweight or small like a lithium-ion battery. In that case, I can only use about half of my capacity, so I'll need a battery that can hold twice the 60 Wh of energy that I'll use each day. A 12 V 10 Ah battery has 120 watt hours of energy (12 volts x 10 amp hours), which is perfect to supply me with the energy I need for one night of use. Just to be safe though, let's go with a 12 V 20 Ah battery so we can be prepared for cloudy days. A 12 V 20 Ah battery shouldn't cost much more than $30-40. If you can only find 10 Ah batteries, which are more common, you can always wire two in parallel to create your own 12 V 20 Ah battery.

Now I'll need a solar panel. If I assume 6 hours of sunlight per day, I would require a 10 watt panel to provide 60 Wh of energy per day. Of course we won't get our full 10 watts out of that panel unless we lived in a perfect world, so let's bump it up to a 15 watt panel. That way, our actual power will be closer to 10 real world watts.

Lastly, we'll need a charge controller. Since I'm using a simple 12 V system and low power, a cheap PWM charge controller is fine for me. It won't be quite as efficient as a MPPT charge controller, but this is just a backyard lighting setup and the difference in energy savings wouldn't even come close to covering the higher cost of the MPPT charge controller. A cheap 12 V and 3 A PWM charge controller costs around $5 from China. At 15 watts and 12 V, I'll barely be pulling 1 A of current, so I am staying well within the specs of nearly any cheap charge controller.

I'll mount the 15 watt panel, which measures around 14" x 14" (350 mm x 350 mm), on a post near my seating area, which will also support one of my lights. I'll angle the panel south (since I am I the northern hemisphere) and aim it approximately at the sun's angle just before midday. I could

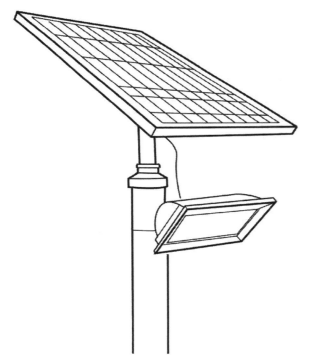

consult charts and solar calculators for my area, but again, we're working with a tiny amount of power here. There difference is going to be measured in milliwatts.

The panel's output will be connected to my charge controller's solar input port. I can just use the stock wires that came on the solar panel, and I'll mount the charge controller right behind the panel, or with the battery, depending on the length of the wires and whichever is more convenient. Next, I'll wire the battery port on the charge controller to the positive and negative leads on my battery, and put my battery in a sealed box such as a plastic storage bin. Since I'm using a sealed lead acid (SLA) battery, I don't have to worry about coming out and checking the acid levels because the battery requires no maintenance. I could even sink the box in at ground level at the base of the post and cover with a little piece of sod if I wanted to hide it from view.

Lastly, I'll connect the load port on the charge controller to my three 12 VDC 5 W LED flood lights. All three sets of wires coming from the three lights will be connected to the load port, or they could be wired in parallel and connected by a single set of wires, depending again on the spacing and convenience.

And that's it - I'm done! Now I have LED flood lights that are powered from a small 12 V 20 Ah SLA battery bank that gets recharged every day from the sun. No extension cords, no ugly wires running across my lawn, and no maintenance! If I ever had an extended period of clouds and ran my batteries down too far, I could always bring them over to a charger and top off them off from the grid, but short of that I am smooth sailing with a maintenance free backyard solar lighting system!

If you ever wanted to build a fancy tree house, complete with lighting and a few creature comforts that electricity can provide, this could be an excellent way to do it, provided you can mount your solar panel somewhere that isn't too shaded by the tree.

Chapter 13: Takeaway

Congratulations, you've made it to the end! If you read this entire book in order, then you've covered everything from the introductory concepts of solar electricity, the design and planning stage of large and small solar projects, and all the way to the process of installing and operating solar power systems.

I hope that you found this book helpful and that it has inspired you to begin your own solar powered projects in the future. With all of this abundant energy from the sun, it is our responsibility to make use of it and not let it go to waste.

I also sincerely hope that you heed the safety warnings spread liberally around this book. Solar power has the potential to create great change in our world, but it can also be dangerous when used improperly. These systems can create large amounts of power, and large battery banks store immense amounts of energy in one place. Please be responsible when working with any of these parts. Don't attempt anything that is outside of your skillset. Always consult with a professional when necessary to ensure that you are following all relevant safety practices and conforming to local laws and codes.

And most of all, enjoy powering your world with solar energy!

Help support independent authors!

I truly hope that you enjoyed this book and that you found it helpful and educational. If so, I'd love if you could leave an honest review of the book on Amazon.com. This would help me to grow my audience and teach even more people about the values of solar energy! Just remember, with every five-star review, an author gets his or her wings!

Acknowledgements

I must start by thanking my wife for putting up with me, not just while I wrote this book, but also for years of finding half completed batteries, solar panel projects and other opened/dismembered electronics laying all around the house with "danger – do NOT touch!" signs on them. My parents taught me to follow my dreams and not stop until I could say that I'd either accomplished my goal or proudly gave it everything I had. I appreciate everything they've done for me and gratefully acknowledge that if I'm a decent person then it is purely a result of their excellent parenting. My dad started me on my journey to becoming a maker, and when I went off to college, my mentor Andy Holmes picked it up from there. I think I learned more from working in Andy's shop than I did from my entire engineering degree. And I learned a LOT from my engineering degree. Lastly, I am sincerely grateful for the countless friends and acquaintances that have crossed my meandering path in life, who have worked on projects with me, taught me things, let me teach them things, and all had an impact in some way, shape or form in how I reached this current point in life today. If a butterfly flapping its wings can impact the formation and path of a distant tornado, then who can ever say how I would have ended up without all of you impacting my life.

About the author

Micah Toll is a mechanical engineer and entrepreneur with nearly a decade of experience in the electric vehicle and lithium battery industry. Micah's books *The Ultimate DIY Ebike Guide* and *DIY Lithium Batteries: How To Build Your Own Battery Packs* have sold thousands of copies all over the world. Micah believes in the principle of "Don't buy what you can make" and promotes a maker-lifestyle based on handiness, resourcefulness and skill collecting. He currently lives in Tel Aviv with his beautiful wife Sapir and his dog Seven.

References:

Deep Cycle Batteries for Solar & Renewable Energy Applications. Retrieved from https://www.wholesalesolar.com/deep-cycle-solar-batteries#lg-chem

Gregersen, S. D. (2014). *Build your own low-budget solar power system.* CreateSpace Independent Publishing Platform

How a Solar Cell Works. Retrieved from https://www.acs.org/content/acs/en/education/resources/highschool/chemmatters/past-issues/archive-2013-2014/how-a-solar-cell-works.html

How much power does the sun give us? Retrieved from http://www.yourturn.ca/solar/solar-power/how-much-power-does-the-sun-give-us/

Knier, G. How Do Photovoltaics Work? Retrieved from https://science.nasa.gov/science-news/science-at-nasa/2002/solarcells

Lowe, D. (2017). *Electronics all-in-one for dummies.* Hoboken, NJ: John Wiley & Sons, Inc.

Maehlum, M. Which Solar Panel Type is Best? Mono- vs. Polycrystalline vs. Thin Film. (2017, August 05). Retrieved from http://energyinformative.org/best-solar-panel-monocrystalline-polycrystalline-thin-film/

MPPT vs PWM Solar Controllers. (2017, October 04). Retrieved from http://www.enerdrive.com.au/mppt-vs-pwm-solar-controllers/

OConnor, J. P. (2016). *Off grid solar: a handbook for photovoltaics with lead-acid or lithium-ion batteries.* San Francisco, CA

Sangur, S. (2013, September 11). AC and DC Electric Shock Effects Compared. Retrieved from http://www.brighthubengineering.com/power-plants/89792-ac-and-dc-shock-comparison/

Smets, A. H., Jäger, K., Isabella, O., Swaaij, R. A., & Zeman, M. (2016). *Solar energy: the physics and engineering of photovoltaic conversion, technologies and systems.* Cambridge, England: UIT Cambridge Ltd.

Smith, E. W. (2011). *DIY solar projects: how to put the sun to work in your home.* Minneapolis, MN: Creative Pub. International.

Solar Energy in Israel FAQ - Frequently Asked Questions - Solar Water Heaters. (2008, July 16). Retrieved from http://www.solar.co.il/water-heaters.htm

Solar Sizing Calculator | Solar Cable Gauge Calculator | Battery Interconnect Calculator - Renogy Solar. Retrieved from https://www.renogy.com/calculators/

The History of Solar [PDF]. US Department of Energy. https://www1.eere.energy.gov/solar/pdfs/solar_timeline.pdf

Made in the USA
San Bernardino, CA
20 June 2019